MODULAR PRACTICE

 NEW YORK · LONDON

JOHN WILEY & SONS, INC.

PREPARED BY:

MODULAR BUILDING STANDARDS ASSOCIATION
FOUNDED BY: AMERICAN INSTITUTE OF ARCHITECTS
ASSOCIATED GENERAL CONTRACTORS OF AMERICA
NATIONAL ASSOCIATION OF HOME BUILDERS
PRODUCERS' COUNCIL, INC.

PROJECT GRANT FROM:

EDUCATIONAL FACILITIES LABORATORIES, INC.

ADMINISTERED BY:

BUILDING RESEARCH ADVISORY BOARD
NATIONAL ACADEMY OF SCIENCES-NATIONAL RESEARCH COUNCIL

MODULAR PRACTICE

THE SCHOOLHOUSE AND THE BUILDING INDUSTRY

EDITORIAL TEAM:

ROBERT P. DARLINGTON, A.I.A., CHIEF EDITOR
FORMERLY ASSOCIATE PROFESSOR OF ARCHITECTURAL ENGINEERING
WASHINGTON STATE UNIVERSITY—ASSISTANT DIRECTOR FOR PROGRAM TRAINING
BUILDING RESEARCH ADVISORY BOARD
NATIONAL ACADEMY OF SCIENCES—NATIONAL RESEARCH COUNCIL

MELVIN W. ISENBERG, P.E., ASSOCIATE EDITOR
PROFESSOR OF ENGINEERING
THE PENNSYLVANIA STATE UNIVERSITY

DAVID A. PIERCE, A.I.A., ASSOCIATE EDITOR
ARCHITECT, COLUMBUS, OHIO
CONSULTANT, OHIO STATE BOARD OF EDUCATION

120456

The title page photograph shows a section of the
Flint School District Administration Building in
Flint, Michigan. Architects-engineers were
Linn Smith Associates, Inc. (formerly Smith, Tarapata,
MacMahon, Inc.) of Birmingham, Michigan. (*Photograph
courtesy of Lens-Art Photographers, Detroit, Michigan.*)

LIBRARY OF CONGRESS CATALOG CARD NUMBER: 62-10918
PRINTED IN THE UNITED STATES OF AMERICA

The "schoolhouse" faces a crisis.

The problem can be seen in the cold figures of population statistics, which point to an increase in the population of the United States from 180,000,000 in 1961 to over 200,000,000 in 1970, and possibly to more than 320,000,000 in the year 2000. It can be seen also in our expanding cities and suburbs, our increasing traffic, our crowded classrooms. More people require more facilities; and, because the increase in population starts at the bottom, with children, this means more educational facilities from the elementary up through the highest levels.

No increase in the efficiency and productivity of any one segment of the building industry, such as in educational facilities, will solve the problem of providing enough buildings of all kinds to catch up to and to keep up with the demands of an exploding population. Housing is needed, together with industrial, commercial, scientific, military, and recreational facilities. But because of the immediate and extreme demand for educational facilities, the focus of this book is on the application of modular practice to the design and construction of the schoolhouse in all its many forms, dormitories as well as classrooms, administrative areas as well as cafeterias, research buildings as well as gymnasia. In this respect, the application of the modular system to all building types is implicit in the discussion of school buildings.

Quantity alone is not a sufficient answer to the need for school buildings. Advancing concepts of education and increasing sophistication in public taste call for facilities of higher quality and greater complexity. The task is made more difficult by the growing demands from other sources for every dollar. The temptation is strong to provide enough educational space at the sacrifice of quality, a policy which, if followed, would have serious, long-range, detrimental effects on our educational system and our national character. The Committee believes that modular practice can contribute substantially to the upgrading of quality as well as to the reduction of costs of school buildings. In meeting both these requirements, modular practice will be of benefit to the school board faced with the task of providing, at the lowest possible cost, high-quality schools which will be satisfactory to the taxpayer.

FOREWORD

The taxpayer will benefit, by receiving more value for his dollar. And the children, for whom schools are actually built, will benefit in terms of good, uncrowded accommodations, and an environment more conducive to learning.

The construction industry contributes significantly to the gross national product and to the development and improvement of our environment. Its role becomes increasingly more dynamic as it responds more quickly to developments in building science and technology and to the needs for new, better, and more complex facilities. This trend must continue at all stages of the building process if the challenge is to be met. The designing of buildings must be as rapid as is feasible for good results. There must be minimum waste in the manufacture of building materials and products. Construction time must be shortened, and wasteful assembly practices eliminated.

In the field of school design and construction, stock plans often have been proposed as a means of achieving the objective of more facilities at less cost. However, the value of stock plans in the creative development of educational facilities has just as often been questioned. The answer probably lies somewhere between the rigid use of stock plans and completely uncontrolled, uncorrelated development and utilization of materials. Modular coordination of materials and components, with some standardization of sizes carefully worked out to retain design freedom for the architect, provides a positive means of producing more and better schools, faster and more economically. Working with modular dimensions and within a framework of coordinated sizes, the architect can design more rapidly and can produce simpler, clearer working drawings in less time. The contractor has found that he can prepare his bid more quickly, that he has less cutting, fitting, and patching and less waste of materials during the building process, and that he is aided in layout and erection by the inherent precision of modular materials and modular coordination.

There has long been an historical concern with modules and systems of proportion, from both the aesthetic and the construction points of view. A number of systems, reaching back as far as the ancient Greeks, are discussed in Appendix F. Concentration in the modern era has been on the use of a small module in the coordination of materials and the standardization of sizes. Most attention has been given in the United States and Canada to the 4-inch module. Neither the Committee nor the editorial team which prepared the book was committed to the exclusive use of the 4-inch module, but upon investigation found it to be the furthest

advanced of any system in use. As a result, emphasis is given in the body of the text to the application of the 4-inch modular system.

The application of modular principles to the reduction of building construction costs has been the subject of study in the United States since the early 1920's. At that time Albert Farwell Bemis, an American industrialist, started research into the dimensional coordination of building materials and equipment in an effort to improve the existing uneconomic methods of assembling unrelated materials. At about the same time Fred Heath authored a Bachelor of Science thesis at the University of Washington on the optimum nominal dimensions of masonry units, and Ernest Flagg undertook a study of the rational relationship between modular principles and architectural design. In 1934, the movement toward modular coordination was promoted by the National Bureau of Standards of the United States Department of Commerce. In 1945, the American Standards Association approved the 4-inch module as an American standard suitable for dimensional coordination. In 1953, eleven European countries, working through the European Productivity Agency of the Organization for European Economic Cooperation, joined in efforts to establish a European module. Their work resulted in recommendation of a module of 10 centimeters, which is very close in size to the American 4-inch module.

Currently, the American Institute of Architects, the Associated General Contractors of America, the National Association of Home Builders, and the Producers' Council sponsor the Modular Building Standards Association to promote modular practice in the United States. It was MBSA which was asked to work with the Building Research Advisory Board of the National Academy of Sciences-National Research Council in preparing this book on modular practice. The grant for the project was made to the Academy-Research Council by the Educational Facilities Laboratories, Inc., a nonprofit corporation established by the Ford Foundation in 1958 to help American schools and colleges with their physical problems by the encouragement of research and experimentation and the dissemination of knowledge regarding educational facilities. The specific interest of the Educational Facilities Laboratories, Inc., in the project stemmed from the conviction that modular practice will make possible more economical, better-quality educational facilities.

The Building Research Advisory Board, following its customary practice, appointed an Advisory Committee composed of representatives of several major segments of the building industry to help plan the project, to advise on its conduct, and to review and evaluate the text material and drawings at regular intervals during the preparation of the manuscript.

The editorial team chosen to prepare the book was selected on the basis of professional interest and lack of bias regarding any specific aspect of dimensional coordination or modular practice. Robert P. Darlington brought to the project several years of architectural practice and eight years in architectural education and research. Melvin W. Isenberg has taught architectural engineering for more than 20 years, including the teaching of modular principles since 1950, and has conducted a private practice as a registered Architectural Engineer for a number of years. David A. Pierce has had his own architectural firm since 1951 and, since 1956, has served as consulting architect to the Ohio State Board of Education on state-aid school projects.

This team traveled extensively throughout the United States and Canada to visit architectural and engineering firms and school construction projects. Its purpose was to uncover the actual working experience of architects, engineers, and contractors with modular practice, to observe the efficiencies and economies of such practice in operation, and to organize in usable form the best of current practice. *Modular Practice* is the result of their efforts.

The Committee can only hazard a guess as to the extent of beneficial results if modular practice were universally accepted by the building industry. Suffice it to say that results would be dramatic. Probably the chief obstacles to widespread acceptance in the past have been the confusions about modular practice resulting from the lack of a clear-cut explanation and demonstration of its techniques and lack of documented proof of its benefits. *Modular Practice* should go far toward removing these obstacles. Later editions of the book will enable new material to be incorporated together with extended specific references to benefits of modular practice in action.

The Committee believes that economy and improved quality in school building design will be achieved through continued freedom of design on the part of the architectural profession; through the coordination of sizes of building materials, products, and components by the manufacturers; and through the understanding and acceptance of these concepts by the contractor in the construction of buildings. It believes also that *Modular Practice* succeeds in presenting the principles and techniques of modular design and construction in a way that will further progress toward the goal of better, more economical schools and, thus, in meeting one of the critical challenges posed by the population explosion and by our demand for a constantly higher level of human achievement.

BUILDING RESEARCH ADVISORY BOARD
ADVISORY COMMITTEE ON MODULAR PRACTICE

Washington, D. C.
February, 1962

BUILDING RESEARCH
ADVISORY BOARD
ADVISORY COMMITTEE
ON MODULAR PRACTICE

CHAIRMAN

Robert B. Taylor
Director, Structural Clay Products Research Foundation
Geneva, Illinois

MEMBERS

William A. Klinger
President, W. A. Klinger, Inc.
Constructor
Sioux City, Iowa

C. M. Lambe
Manager, Research Department
United States Gypsum Company
Chicago, Illinois

Robert F. Legget
Director, Division of Building Research
National Research Council of Canada
Ottawa, Canada

Edward J. Losi
Cosentini Associates
Mechanical Engineers
New York, New York

Paul Rudolph, AIA
Chairman, Department of Architecture
Yale University
New Haven, Connecticut

Donald Kenneth Sargent, FAIA
Dean, School of Architecture
Syracuse University
Syracuse, New York

John Stanley Sharp, AIA
Ketchum and Sharp
Architects
New York, New York

Herbert H. Swinburne, FAIA
Nolen and Swinburne
Architects
Philadelphia, Pennsylvania

(Alternate to Mr. Legget)
Stanley R. Kent
Assistant Professor, School of Architecture
University of Toronto
Toronto, Ontario

SECRETARY

Robert M. Dillon, AIA
Executive Director, Building Research Advisory Board
National Academy of Sciences-National Research
    Council
Washington, D. C.

A child's set of building blocks is made up of units which are multiples of the smallest piece in the set. If they were not, and the child were required to cut and fit each piece whenever he attempted to build a tower, he would soon turn to other activities, and the manufacturer of the blocks would not long have a market.

On a far larger scale, the application of this principle to the sizing of building materials or components as multiples of a common size also seems reasonable; yet the building industry, because of its complexity and scope of operation, has thus far failed to achieve any large-scale degree of coordination in the sizing of the thousands of products involved. Where coordination has been worked out on the basis of a common unit size, or module, and has been carried through from the design of a building to its construction, the amounts of time and labor saved have indicated that widespread use of the method would result in substantial cost savings. In addition, the use of modular coordination has shown that quality is improved in the final structure through elimination of much of the cutting, fitting, and patching which are often necessary with non-coordinated, or nonmodular, materials. The building owner thus benefits in terms of lower cost, shorter construction time, and improved quality and appearance.

The problems of the building industry in meeting the challenge to educational and other facilities which is posed by the rapidly expanding population have been discussed in the Foreword. Other factors, in addition to the population increase, have a bearing on the design and construction of school buildings. The total number of students attending school is increasing, not only because of the increase in population, but also because the *percentage* of those attending high school and college is rising. Recent estimates maintain that the total university physical plant in the United States must double in the 1960–1970 decade to meet the influx of new students. Accompanying the purely quantitative increase in educational buildings is a demand for facilities of higher quality and of greater versatility and flexibility, to accommodate the requirements of new educational techniques and philosophies.

Modular Practice presents the application of

PREFACE

modular principles to the design and construction of educational facilities as one way in which the building industry can substantially increase its productivity. As used by the architect, modular practice consists of *modular design, modular coordination,* and *modular dimensioning. Modular design* involves planning in terms of spatial and material coordination throughout the period of creative design, starting with the first schematic sketches. *Modular coordination* is the dimensional and constructional organization of building materials and components which have been sized on the basis of a common small dimensional unit. *Modular dimensioning* of the working drawings is the means of assuring the accurate construction of the coordinated modular design by showing the coordination through simple dimensions which relate all parts of a structure to the coordinating system.

Recognition of the value of modular practice has come from a number of states and from various agencies. The Pennsylvania State Council of Education requires that all state-aid schools be planned on modular principles and constructed of modular materials and components. In Wisconsin, the Office of the State Architect is urging that all state work be modular. For a number of years, the Office of the Chief of Engineers in Washington, D. C., has requested modular practice for most of its buildings, and in 1958 the Veterans Administration changed to modular practice in the design of all new hospitals. In 1957, Congress passed laws requiring the use of modular practice in public housing, low-rent housing, and military housing. There will undoubtedly be increasingly broader applications throughout the industry as architects, manufacturers, and contractors become aware of the simplicities and economies inherent in the use of modular practice.

The preparation of *Modular Practice* for publication would not have been possible without the grant from the Educational Facilities Laboratories, Inc., to the National Academy of Sciences-National Re-

search Council. The editors wish to express their appreciation to EFL for the grant, and to acknowledge the assistance, cooperation, and advice which they received from many sources. Mr. Robert M. Dillon, AIA, Executive Director of the Building Research Advisory Board, and Mr. Byron C. Bloomfield, AIA, Executive Director of the Modular Building Standards Association, contributed invaluable advice and guidance and considerable amounts of time and effort, both in the early phases of the project and during the actual preparation of the manuscript. Mr. C. E. Silling, FAIA, President of the Modular Building Standards Association, was a constant source of advice and encouragement. The searching criticism and positive suggestions by the members of the Advisory Committee during their reviews of the several drafts of the book proved overwhelmingly the value of a group of dedicated men working toward a common goal.

Much credit for the actual production of the book must go to the personnel of the Modular Building Standards Association office. Mrs. Jean Edes, MBSA Administrative Secretary, was responsible for much of the initial contact work in the development of the project, a great amount of typing and correspondence, and all the bookkeeping. Mr. Geza Schay and Mr. Tod de Kanter performed an extremely capable and conscientious job in preparing the illustrations.

Because of her special contributions to the project in the form of constant cheerfulness and efficiency in the face of an enormous flood of correspondence, and throughout the typing of the several drafts of the manuscript, a special expression of appreciation is made to Mr. Darlington's secretary, Mrs. Frieda Arth.

ROBERT P. DARLINGTON, AIA
MELVIN W. ISENBERG, PE
DAVID A. PIERCE, AIA

Washington, D. C.
February, 1962

The editors of *Modular Practice* wish to emphasize the excellent quality of the cooperation offered
by the many firms which they visited while collect-
ing information on the techniques and benefits of
modular practice. It would be impossible to list all
the individuals who contributed time and advice,
but the editors wish to acknowledge the assistance given by the following firms, groups, and
individuals:

C. E. Silling and Associates, Architects, Charleston, West
    Virginia
Nolen and Swinburne, Architects, Philadelphia, Penn-
    sylvania
Carl Koch and Associates, Architects, Cambridge,
    Massachusetts
The Architects Collaborative, Architects, Cambridge,
    Massachusetts
Designs for Business, Inc., New York, New York
Skidmore, Owings, and Merrill, Architects, New York,
    New York
I. M. Pei Associates, Architects, New York, New York
Sargent, Webster, Crenshaw and Folley, Architects and
    Engineers, Syracuse, N. Y.
Moulton and Van Keuren, Architect Associates, Syra-
    cuse, New York
Pederson, Hueber and Hares, Architects, and Glavin,
    Landscape Architect, Syracuse, New York
Page and Steele, Architects, Toronto, Ontario
Vine and Robinson, Architects, Toronto, Ontario
Aeck Associates, Architects, Atlanta, Georgia
Bull and Kenney, Architects, Atlanta, Georgia
Lionel H. Abshire and Associates, Architects, Baton
    Rouge, Louisiana
Architectural Research Section, Southwest Research In-
    stitute, San Antonio, Texas
Kistner, Wright and Wright, Architects, Los Angeles,
    California
Smith, Powell and Morgridge, Architects, Los Angeles,
    California
Allison and Rible, Architects, Los Angeles, California
Herman Charles Light, Architect, Los Angeles, Cali-
    fornia
Edward Hale Fickett, Architect, Los Angeles, California
Deasy and Bolling, Architects, Los Angeles, California
George Vernon Russell, Architect, Los Angeles, Cali-
    fornia
Daniel, Mann, Johnson and Mendenhall, Inc., Archi-
    tects-Engineers, Los Angeles, California
Department of Architecture, College of Environmental
    Design, University of California, Berkeley, California

ACKNOWLEDGMENTS

John Carl Warnecke and Associates, Architects, San Francisco, California

Reid, Rockwell, Banwell and Tarics, Architects and Engineers, San Francisco, California

Robert Billsbrough Price, Architect, Tacoma, Washington

Lea, Pearson and Richards, Architects, Tacoma, Washington

Brown and Wright Associates, Architects, Washington, D. C.

Architectural Section, Structures Branch, Office of the Chief of Engineers, Washington, D. C.

Linn Smith Associates, Inc., Architects, Birmingham, Michigan

Tarapata-MacMahon-Associates, Inc., Architects and Engineers, Bloomfield Hills, Michigan

John J. Flad and Associates, Architects and Engineers, Madison, Wisconsin

State Architect's Office, Madison, Wisconsin

Weiler and Strang, Architects, Madison, Wisconsin

Perkins and Will, Architects-Engineers, Chicago, Illinois

John R. Magney, Architect, Minneapolis, Minnesota

The photographs at the beginning of the chapters were supplied by the following:

Chapter 1:
Herbert H. Swinburne
Philadelphia, Pennsylvania

Chapter 2:
C. E. Silling and Associates
Charleston, West Virginia

Chapter 3:
Johnson and Shirk, Inc.
Birmingham, Michigan

Chapter 4:
Gabriel Benzur
Atlanta, Georgia

Chapter 5:
C. E. Silling and Associates
Charleston, West Virginia

Chapter 6:
Lionel H. Abshire & Associates
Baton Rouge, Louisiana

Chapter 7:
Lens-Art Photographers
Detroit, Michigan

Chapter 8:
Herbert H. Swinburne
Philadelphia, Pennsylvania

Chapter 9:
Joseph W. Molitor
Ossining, New York

Chapter 10:
Dandelet Photographs
San Anselmo, California

CONTENTS

Temple University Men's Dormitories
Philadelphia, Pennsylvania

Nolen and Swinburne
Architects
Philadelphia, Pennsylvania

Greater productive capacity in the construction industry to meet the demands of an expanding population must be provided by increases in efficiency in the processes and techniques of designing and building. An ultimate objective is the development of a system of construction in which all materials, components, products, and equipment fit together simply and easily with minimum alterations required on the job. Such a system involves:

1. A design philosophy which requires that the architect think in terms of complete dimensional coordination at all stages of the design process.

2. A method of portraying the coordination graphically in the working drawings.

3. A system of sizing building products in conformity with a module which permits their dimensional coordination.

4. Construction techniques which capitalize on the coordination of materials in the building design.

These requirements are basic in the concept of modular coordination. The actual process of coordination is applied to the design of a building by the architect as he considers the required functions of the spaces of a building, the materials available, and the possible structural, electrical, and mechanical systems, and relates them through use of a common dimensional unit. These relationships are then shown on the working drawings by means of a simple dimensioning system which differentiates between the location of materials which are on the basic module and those which are not. Wherever possible, materials are used which have been sized as multiples of the basic module; and, in construction, layout and assembly techniques are employed which utilize the coordination designed into the structure to minimize the amount of cutting and fitting required on the job.

The word "module," which derives from the Latin *modulus,* meaning measure, does not itself denote a specific size. This has led to some confusion when the term has been applied to dimensional coordination in building. In 1945, the American Standards Association adopted a basic module of 4 inches to encourage the use of a single basic module for every building, and to provide a basis for the sizing of materials and components. When these products are produced in conformity with the basic 4-inch coordinating unit, all building dimensions can be established during the early stages of a design solution as multiples of 4 inches with the assurance that the majority of the products finally chosen for the building can be coordinated with these dimensions with a minimum of effort. The

1

THE
ELEMENTS
OF
MODULAR
PRACTICE

4-inch module is small enough to allow flexibility of design, and the techniques of the modular-dimensioning system make divergence from this module possible when necessary.

GRID TYPES

The basic tool used by the architect in the development and expression of a coordinated modular design is the grid, which is defined in Webster's *New International Dictionary* as "a grating or gridiron, or something resembling or likened to one." In the context of this book, a grid is a network of lines, running both horizontally and vertically, from which the measurements and the positions of building components may be determined. Several types of grids, each with a specific function, may be used in the design and coordination of a building. Successful use of the modular system requires the coordination of these grids. *Each grid type should be considered as a tool to aid, not to dictate, the development of a design solution.* In practice, the majority of architects prefer to work as freely as possible in developing the best plan solution, arriving first at general modular dimensions and then adopting the specific dimensions that are necessary to ensure modular coordination.

Planning grid. The *planning grid,* sometimes called the "design grid," is the basic means of achieving a logical and controlled plan solution. It is a repetitive shape developed from a basic functional requirement of the plan and is used for the general layout of the major rooms and other spaces in a building. In the planning of a school building, not all the required areas can be based easily on the same planning grid. A specific functional area such as a high-school drafting room could be developed from a planning grid based on the space requirements of a draftsman: size of drafting table, stool, reference area, aisle space, and storage. This planning grid would probably be different in size, shape, and dimensions from the grid used to lay out a classroom or other teaching space, which might be based on the total area required per student. However, if the dimensions of the various planning grids are multiples of the basic 4-inch module, the modular approach is established early in the design phase.

Greater simplicity in design and structure is usually possible if a single planning grid can be applied to an entire project. This is particularly true if the planning grid is coordinated with the structural system of a building. When the planning grid fits repetitively into the rhythmic pattern of the structural elements, production of the working drawings and construction of the building are both simplified. If planning grids of different sizes or shapes are required in the same building, it is desirable that they be multiples of the 4-inch module and that they coincide at specific points for modular continuity and development of over-all modular dimensions.

A planning grid superimposed on a portion of the floor plan of an existing building is shown in Figure 1-1. This illustration is used only to show the concept of the planning grid as applied to the arrangement of interior office space; therefore no dimensions are given.

Structural grid. The *structural grid* is a grid based on the spacing of the vertical supporting elements in a building. It defines the repetitive structural module just as the planning grid defines the planning module. In the design stage it is used for general reference in coordinating plan, structure, and enclosing elements, for determining spans, and for preliminary selection of sizes of structural members. A structural grid in plan is illustrated in Figure 1-2.

The structural system of a building is selected early in the design process as the space requirements of the interior are crystallized and are balanced against aesthetic and economic considerations. *Coordination of plan and structure must take place at this early stage.* The design and construction of the building become more complex if the materials and dimensions are not coordinated and are not modular. Whenever possible, therefore, both the planning grid and the structural grid should be established at an early stage as multiples of 4 inches and should be coordinated so that the planning grid coincides with the structural grid at regular intervals.

Structural grids are frequently shown on working drawings for the purpose of locating and identifying columns and nearby areas. In this sense, they are also reference grids, which are described below. When a structural grid is used on working drawings, it is shown on both plans and elevations for easy visual coordination. Individual structural grid lines are also utilized in wall sections and details for the purpose of establishing exact identification of the area shown in the drawing.

Reference grid. The *reference grid* is developed specifically for use on the working drawings as an additional *means of communication* between the architect, his associates, the engineers, and the contractor to locate and identify areas and details in the building. Frequently it is drawn as a light grid over the whole plan with letter and number co-

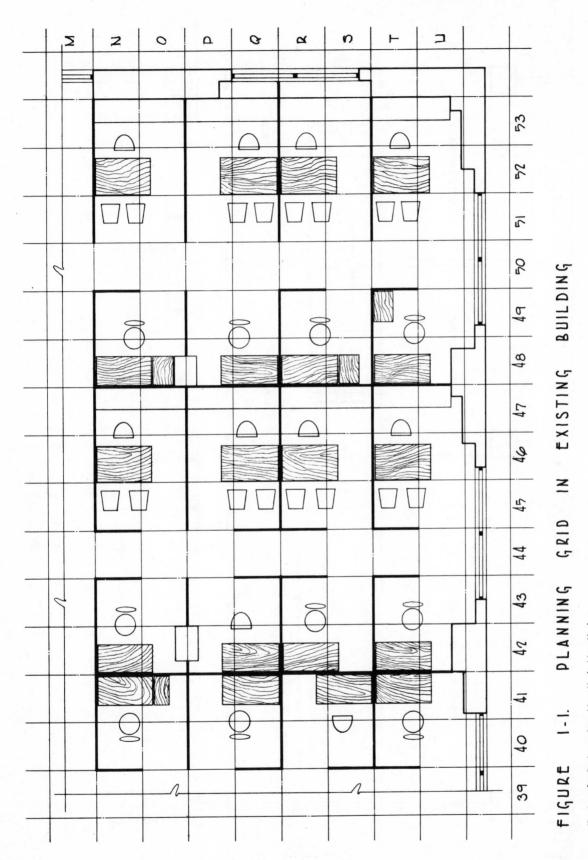

FIGURE 1-1. PLANNING GRID IN EXISTING BUILDING

(Designs for Business, Inc., New York, New York:
Henry Holt and Company Building, New York, New York)

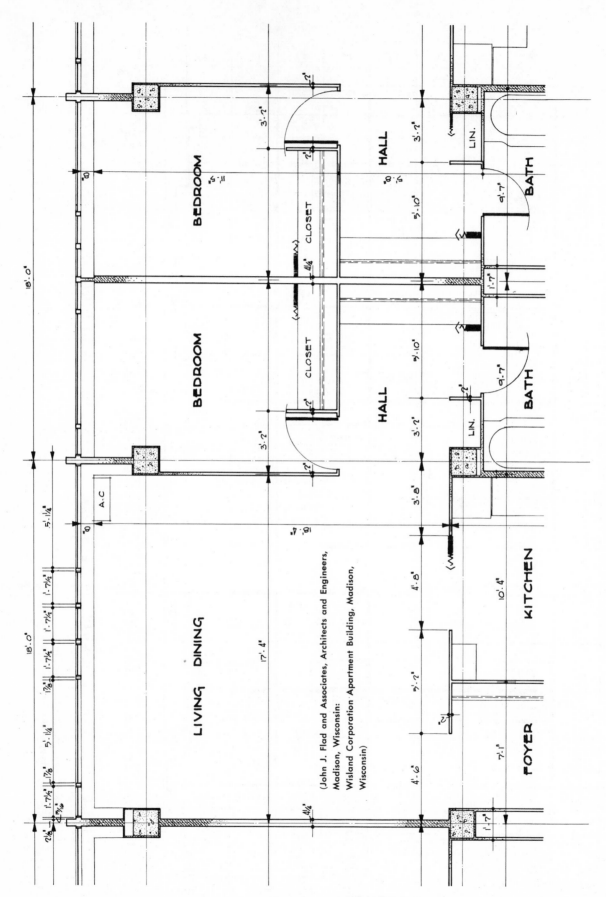

(John J. Flad and Associates, Architects and Engineers, Madison, Wisconsin: Wisland Corporation Apartment Building, Madison, Wisconsin)

FIGURE 1-2. STRUCTURAL GRID IN PLAN

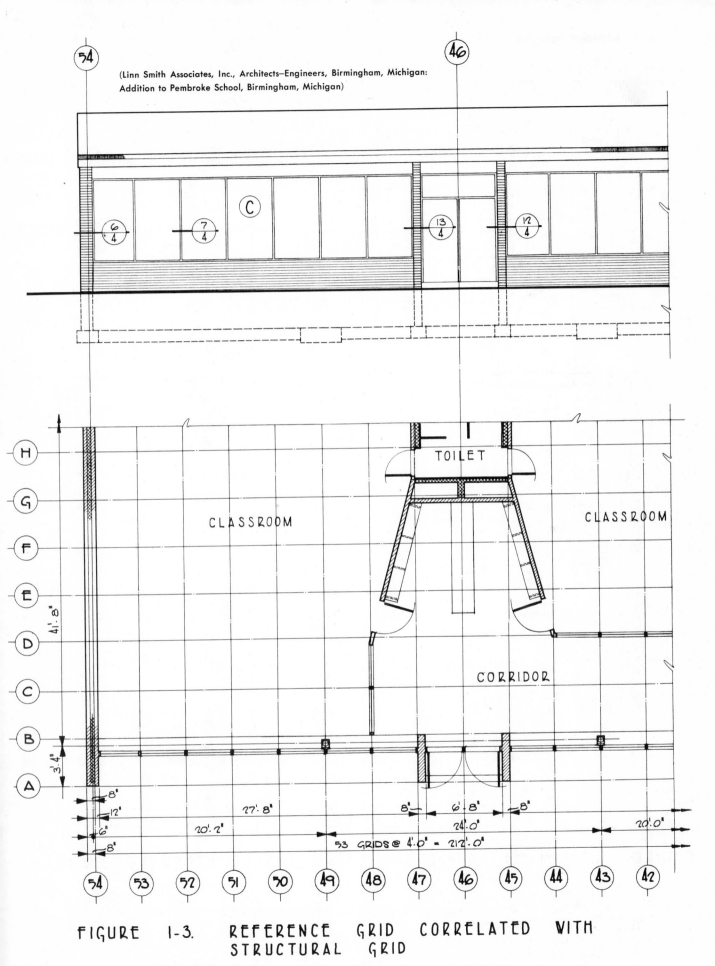

(Linn Smith Associates, Inc., Architects—Engineers, Birmingham, Michigan: Addition to Pembroke School, Birmingham, Michigan)

FIGURE 1-3.   REFERENCE GRID CORRELATED WITH
STRUCTURAL GRID

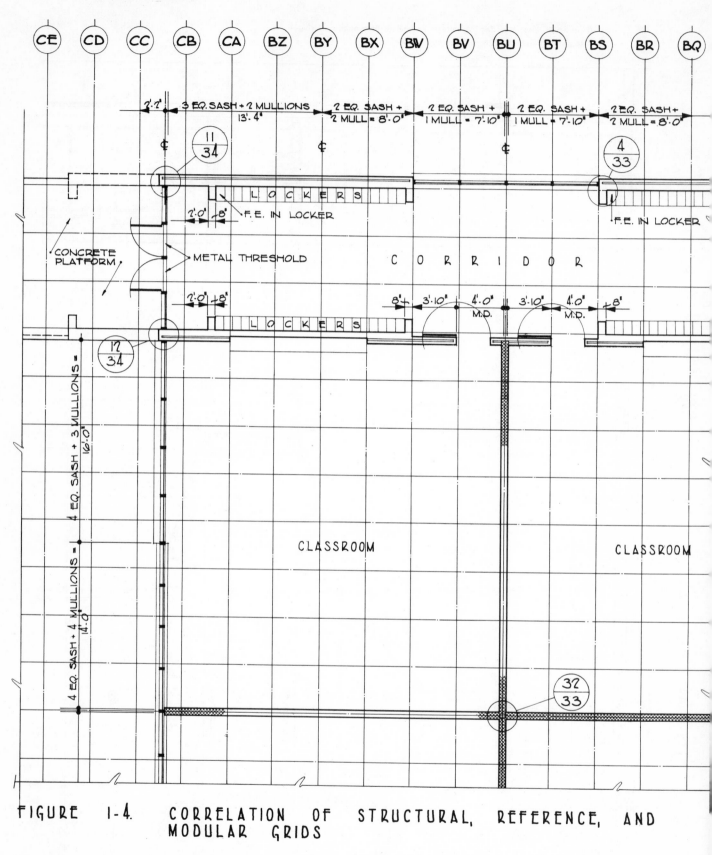

FIGURE 1-4.   CORRELATION OF STRUCTURAL, REFERENCE, AND MODULAR GRIDS

(Linn Smith Associates, Inc. (formerly Smith-Tarapata-MacMahon, Inc.), Architects–Engineers, Birmingham, Michigan: Wylie E. Groves High School, Birmingham, Michigan)

ordinates similar to those on a map. The reference grid is shown only around the outside of a plan, or above or below an elevation, when the additional lines of the grid running through a drawing might cause confusion. In a modular project, the reference grid is a multiple of 4 inches and is usually a regular subdivision of the structural grid. The correlation of reference grid and structural grid in the plan and elevation of a small school is illustrated in Figure 1-3.

Modular grid. The *modular grid* is used to complete the detailed coordination of a design by coordinating the building materials and components and correlating all the dimensions. Maximum coordination is obtained by means of the 4-inch module because the majority of modular materials are sized according to this standard.

The 4-inch module is *visualized* in use as a three-dimensional grid occurring throughout a building. The building's structural and enclosing elements—columns, walls, partitions, beams, slabs, floors, ceilings, doors, windows—are related dimensionally to this grid, and the coordination of materials and components is expressed through reference to it.

Grid lines as reference lines. When a project is coordinated by use of the 4-inch module, all grid types must be coordinated, which means that the modular grid will coincide with the planning grid,

the structural grid, and the reference grid. Some of the modular grid lines, therefore, will also be reference lines and will be shown on the working drawings, establishing the 4-inch multiple at key points throughout the building.

Figure 1-3, which is used to show the coordination of reference and structural grids, will serve also to demonstrate the coordination of the modular grid with the others. The dimensions of the reference grid and the structural grid are multiples of 4 inches, indicating that a 4-inch grid is actually superimposed on the plan and that the 4-inch modular grid and the reference and structural grids coincide. Another example of the correlation of the three grids—structural, reference, and modular—is shown in Figure 1-4.

THE DRAFTING TOOLS

"Thinking modular" must be emphasized as a basic part of modular designing. This approach, and the coordination which results from it, must be expressed clearly in the working drawings for communication with the contractor and all others who use the drawings. This purpose is accomplished by the use of *modular dimensioning*, which is the means of communicating the details of the coordinated design to those who will build the structure.

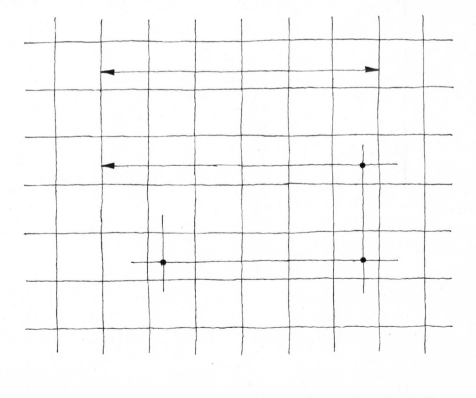

FIGURE 1-5. ARROW AND DOT SYMBOLS

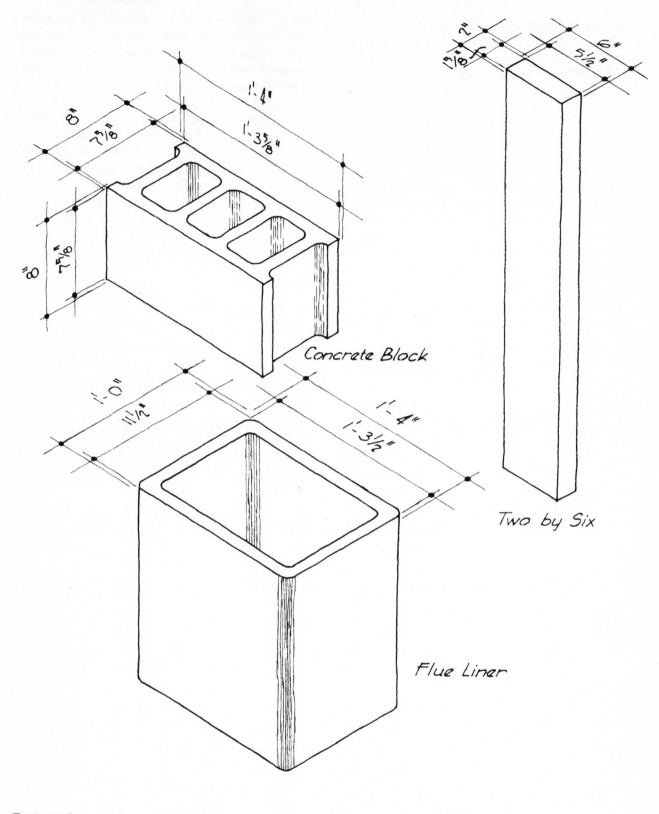

Concrete Block

Two by Six

Flue Liner

FIGURE 1-6. NOMINAL AND ACTUAL SIZES

Grid, arrow, and dot. *The three basic tools of modular dimensioning are:*

1. The 4-inch grid.
2. The dimensioning arrow.
3. The dimensioning dot.

Both arrow and dot are needed because dimensions terminate sometimes on modular grid lines and sometimes at locations off the grid. *An arrow is always used to indicate dimensions to a grid line; a dot, to indicate dimensions to a point off the grid.*

Use of the arrow and dot symbols is shown in Figure 1-5. The upper dimension, terminated at each end by an arrow on a grid line, will always be a modular dimension, that is, a multiple of the grid module. The middle dimension, terminated with an arrow on the grid at one end, and with a dot off the grid at the other end, will never be a multiple of the module and cannot be a modular dimension. The lower dimension, terminated at each end with a dot off the grid, may or may not be a multiple of the module. If it is, it is considered to be a modular dimension, but is still indicated with dots because it terminates off the grid.

Use of the arrow and dot system forestalls any tendency to force construction elements to fall on the grid. The small modular grid itself, which exists primarily in the mind of the architect and may appear only occasionally on the drawings, is a *coordinating and reference tool only.* When the architect decides that a material or a construction element should be located off the grid, he may place it wherever he chooses, and reference it to the grid with an arrow-dot dimension line. In this way, the specific placement of off-grid elements is determined and their location in the scheme is not in doubt.

NOMINAL AND ACTUAL SIZES

The concept of nominal and actual sizes of building materials, components, and products is important in the modular-dimensioning system. The *nominal size* of a material is the size by which it is commonly described, such as a 2 by 4 wood stud or an 8-inch concrete block. The *actual size* of a material is the size which it measures. In the case of the nominal 2 by 4, the actual size is $1\frac{5}{8}$ inches by $3\frac{5}{8}$ inches. The actual size of the 8 by 8 by 16 block is $7\frac{5}{8}$ inches by $7\frac{5}{8}$ inches by $15\frac{5}{8}$ inches. Another example is the modular brick, which is nominally 4 inches wide, $2\frac{2}{3}$ inches high, and 8

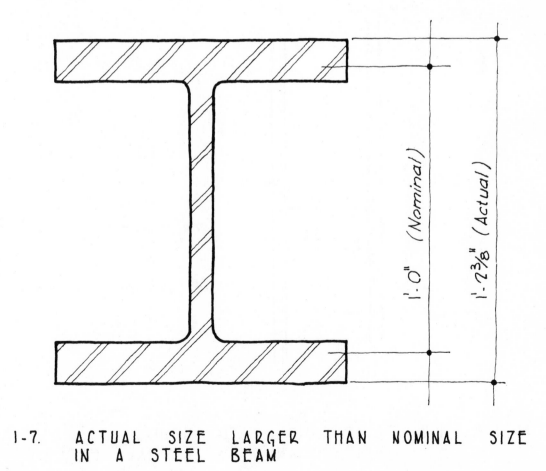

FIGURE 1-7. ACTUAL SIZE LARGER THAN NOMINAL SIZE IN A STEEL BEAM

inches long, but is actually 3⅝ inches by 2³⁄₁₆ inches by 7⅝ inches. Such differences between actual and nominal sizes are understood and accepted throughout the building industry. Working drawing dimensions may be based on either nominal or actual sizes, but for clarity the use of one or the other must be consistent and must be pointed out unmistakably to the contractor. Several examples of nominal and actual sizes of materials are illustrated in Figure 1-6.

Occasionally, the actual size of a material is *larger* than its nominal size. This is the case with the structural steel shape shown in Figure 1-7. A nominal 12-inch-deep steel wide-flange beam can vary in depth from 11.95 inches to 14⅜ inches. These cases are exceptions, but the architect must be aware of them.

Dimensioning to nominal sizes. Nominal sizes of materials are usually nonfractional, whereas actual sizes are frequently fractional. Dimensioning to actual sizes on working drawings thus results in a large number of fractional dimensions. On the other hand, dimensioning to nominal sizes eliminates the need for fractions.

The difference between dimensioning to nominal faces and dimensioning to actual faces is shown in Figure 1-8. A portion of a stud wall is pictured, faced on each side with a sheet material. One stud is shown to indicate its actual size with relation to its nominal size. In this case, it is centered between grid lines, with the grid lines coinciding with the nominal faces. The dimension arrows indicate the location of the grid lines, and the 4-inch dimension gives the nominal thickness of the wall. If dimensions were given to actual stud faces, dots would be used and a fractional dimension of 3⅝ inches would be required to give the actual stud thickness. If the opposite wall of the room were located at a modular distance from this wall, the nominal dimension from wall to wall would eliminate fractions entirely, but dimensions to actual stud faces or to wall finishes would require fractions.

Dimensioning to nominal faces, and locating grid

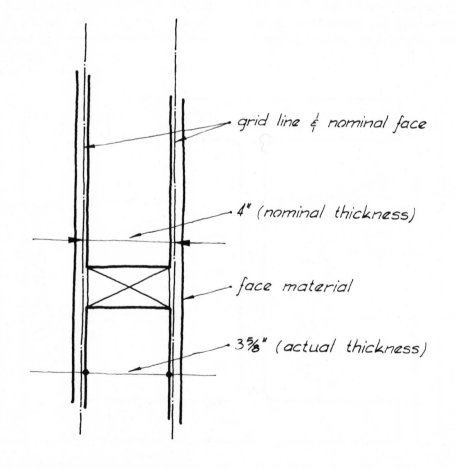

FIGURE 1-8. DIMENSIONING TO NOMINAL FACES (ON GRID LINES) AND TO ACTUAL FACES

lines at nominal faces, are two techniques common to modular dimensioning. When they are used consistently, the production of working drawings is simplified and the drawings are more legible.

DIMENSIONING TECHNIQUES

Dimensions are given on working drawings to enable the builder to locate and place materials in a building as quickly and as easily as possible. Several different modular-dimensioning techniques may be used, the choice between them often depending on local practice as understood by the contractors, the customary practice of a given office, or on which technique gives the most easily read drawings for a specific project. The architect should indicate clearly which method he is using, and employ it consistently throughout the drawings.

Center lines and nominal faces. In modular dimensioning, dimensions are sometimes given to center lines of exterior columns, window mullions, or window openings, and to center lines of interior walls, partitions, or columns. This method gives the least number of dimensions on a drawing, but does not show the sizes of the columns, windows, walls, or openings. When these should be indicated, dimensions are given to their nominal faces to show the nominal sizes of the members and the distance between them. Wherever feasible, grid lines are located on center lines or on the nominal faces to ensure the modular coordination of the project. In Figures 1-9 and 1-10 these techniques are shown as they apply to dimensions at interior partitions.

In Figure 1-9, the arrows indicate that the dimensions are to grid lines. On a small-scale plan, the grid lines themselves are not shown, and a dimension is given to indicate the nominal thickness of the wall, whether it is 4 inches, 8 inches, or larger. If the wall is a nonmodular thickness, such as 6 inches, this nominal thickness is dimensioned, and a dot is used to show which nominal face is not on the grid. In Figure 1-9, the arrows from wall to wall show that the size of the room is modular from nominal face to nominal face.

In Figure 1-10, the grid lines are on the center lines of the partitions, as indicated by the arrows, and nominal sizes and faces are not involved in the dimensioning. This has the advantage of eliminating the wall-thickness dimension at each partition, but the disadvantage of not showing the size of the partition when partitions of different thicknesses are used.

Grid lines at actual faces. A third variation is sometimes used, that of dimensioning to a grid line at the actual face, rather than the nominal face,

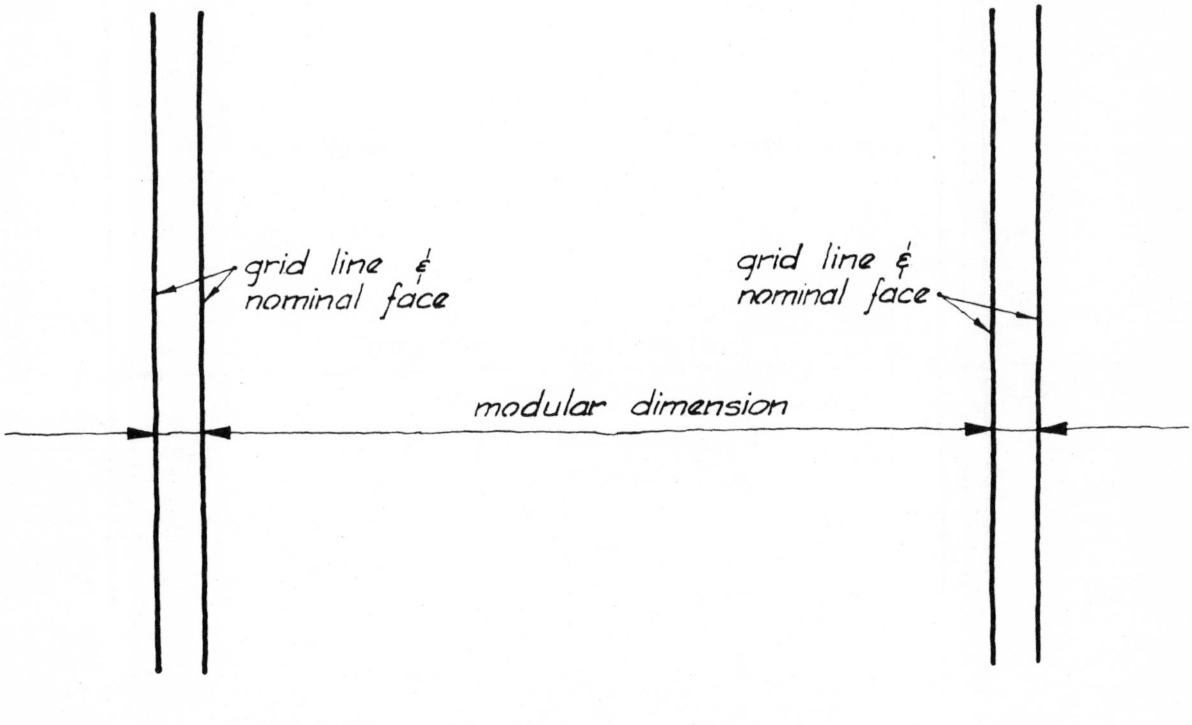

grid line &
nominal face

grid line &
nominal face

modular dimension

FIGURE 1-9. DIMENSIONING GRID LINES AT NOMINAL FACES

on one side only of the stud or block or other partition material. This is illustrated in Figure 1-11. In this case, in order to eliminate the fractional dimensioning of the actual wall thickness and of the room size, dimensions are given to one side of the wall only. If the actual wall thickness is required, it is given separately.

Grid lines at joints. Small modular units of building material, such as bricks or blocks, are manufactured as multiples of 4 inches measured horizontally from center of joint to center of joint. Grid lines, therefore, pass through joint center lines in materials of this type, dimensions are given to the grid lines, and fractional dimensions are avoided.

The same principle is applied to larger components. The actual size of a unit is not critical as long as its over-all size plus a half-joint at each end is a multiple of the small dimensioning module.

The technique of dimensioning to a grid line at the center line of a joint is illustrated in Figure 1-12. In this figure, if the opposite end of either dimension line is assumed to be to the center line of an-

other joint, or to any grid-line location, the dimension is modular and is without fractions. However, if the opposite end is to an off-grid location, the dimension is nonmodular. Dimensioning to joint center lines of a row of modular units is shown in Figure 1-13.

In this sketch the imaginary modular grid has been shown to indicate the relationship of the units to the grid. If a 4-inch grid is assumed, the units shown are nominally 8 inches long. If they were 12-inch nominal units, three grids to a unit would be shown in this sketch, with grid lines at the joint center lines and at the third-points of each unit. On a small-scale working drawing plan neither the grid lines nor the individual units are shown. Standard material indications are used according to the practice of the individual office, and only the arrows at the ends of the dimension lines are needed to indicate the location of the grid lines. At the larger scales used for details in working drawings, the individual units and joints are drawn and dimensioned showing the dimensional relationship of the

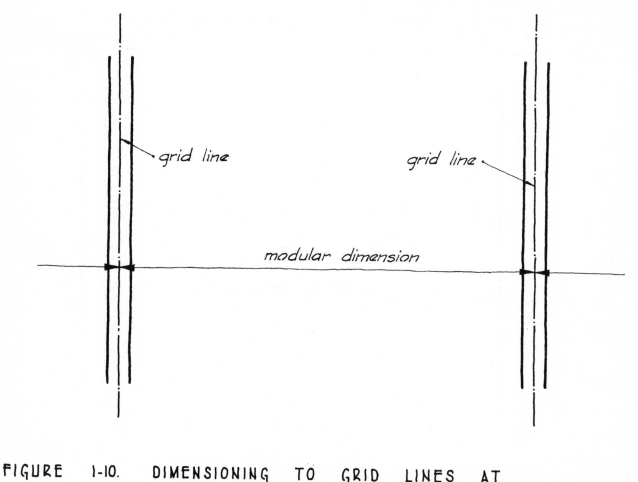

FIGURE 1-10.   DIMENSIONING TO GRID LINES AT CENTER LINES

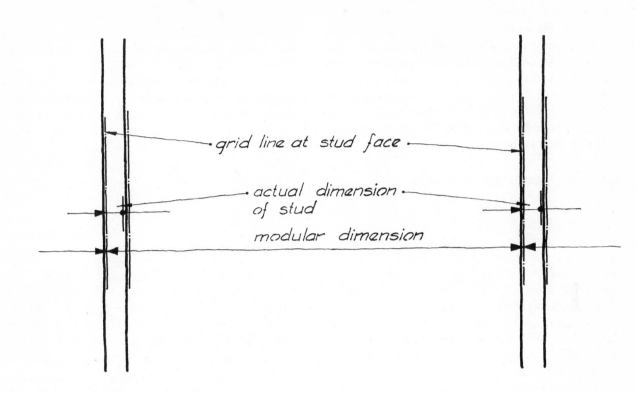

grid line at stud face

actual dimension
of stud

modular dimension

FIGURE I-11.   DIMENSIONING TO GRID LINE AT
              ACTUAL STUD FACE

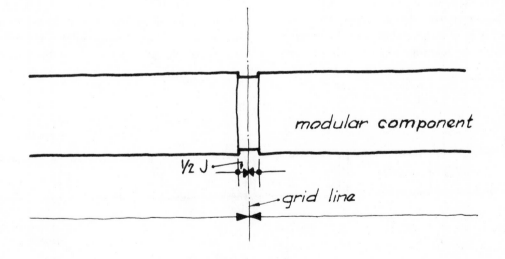

modular component

½ J

grid line

FIGURE I-12.   GRID LINE AT JOINT CENTER LINE

component to the grid, but the only grid lines which need be shown are those necessary for reference and dimensioning.

The illustrations in this chapter are used to show the basic principles of modular dimensioning. Indications of actual materials have purposely been avoided in many of them. More specific treatment of the techniques of modular dimensioning is given in Chapters 4 through 7. Grid lines are shown in the diagrammatic sketches in this chapter only to indicate the relationships involved.

MODULAR PRACTICE IN THE FIELD

Construction tolerances. Construction tolerances are an important consideration in the design and erection of any building. The difficulty of achieving precision in layout, and the normal variation in size of building materials, require that space be allowed in the design of the building to accommodate these variations. Standards are established for maximum and minimum tolerances of building materials. Architects are aware of these tolerances and work within them in detailing the placement of materials and in establishing dimensions. The modular grid aids in utilizing tolerances in the design of a building by serving as the reference system for locating materials precisely.

In the construction phase, key grid lines are located before materials are placed. This forces the proper placement of the materials with respect to the grid and prevents "dimensional creep," which is the gradual accumulation of dimensional errors in the physical placement of materials. Proper tolerances must, of course, be included in the detailed modular component and joint dimensioning to prevent creep caused by the allowance of too little space for the proper placement of materials.

Grids and supervision. Modular construction simplifies the work of the field supervisor through the natural precision and accuracy which accompany the use of the modular grid in construction layout. Surveyors' transits are often utilized to establish the precise location of key reference grid lines in a building as well as the structural grid lines, and these are used to locate accurately the specific modular grid lines which are shown in the details of the working drawing. This constant control virtually eliminates any chance of dimensional error and provides the supervisor with a simple means of checking construction accuracy.

OTHER CONSIDERATIONS

Modular note to contractor. The bidding and construction advantages of modular design will be gained only if the contractor is aware that the drawings are modular and if he understands the principles of modular design and the techniques of modular construction. An explanatory note about modular design and the modular-dimensioning system should be placed on the first sheet of a set of working drawings. Examples of these notes are given in Chapter 4.

Modular explanation. To ensure that all contractors bidding a modular project understand the system, the architect should explain it to those who are not familiar with it before they prepare their bids. After the contract is let, another session should be conducted by the architect to elaborate on the system and on modular-construction techniques for the contractor, the subcontractors, and

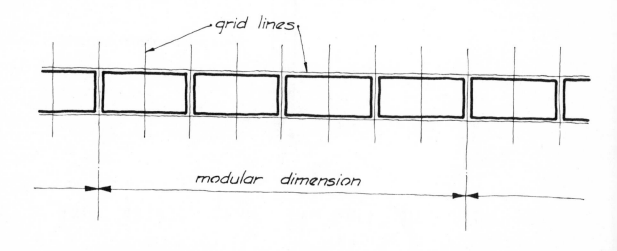

FIGURE 1-13. DIMENSIONING TO JOINT CENTER LINES

their key men. This helps to get the project started properly and eliminates many problems resulting from differences in interpretation of the drawings.

Modular products. Full modular coordination is

Modular Building Standards Association, are identifying their modular products in their literature and sometimes on the products themselves with the following symbol:

▲ Sizes in conformance with the recommendations of the
MODULAR BUILDING STANDARDS ASSOCIATION

possible only when materials and components of all types are produced in conformity with an established system. This requires general agreement, among the producers of building products, on the modular system and on details of jointing. Many modular products are available which are manufactured on the basis of the 4-inch module adopted by the American Standards Association. An increasing number of manufacturers, members of the

The application of modular practice as a means of achieving coordination, simplicity, efficiency, and economy in the design and construction phases of building encourages the further development and use of modular products. The three basic tools, grid, arrow, and dot, applied with discretion to the problems of creative architectural design, provide the specific means of accomplishing more coordination and achieving buildings of higher quality.

College of Agriculture
West Virginia University
Morgantown, West Virginia

C. E. Silling and Associates
Architects
Charleston, West Virginia

The successful architectural solution to a school building problem starts with a statement of the problem itself in the form of a program outlining the school board's requirements. This is basically a statement of the desired function of the building. The architect's responsibility is the achievement of an acceptable functional and aesthetic solution to the program within the limitations of the budget. No technical system of coordinating and portraying a project can replace the ability of a creative designer at any stage of the design process. The architect can, however, benefit from the intelligent use of design aids which assist him in organizing his thinking and in coordinating the results. The modular approach can help in the logical, efficient organization of the building spaces and of the building materials, components, structure, and equipment which define the spaces and service them.

In a successful modular solution, "thinking modular" begins at an early stage of the design process. Generally, this is immediately after the diagrammatic studies of functional relationships which determine the most appropriate organization of the required areas of the building. At this stage, there should be a general, rather than a restrictive, application of the principles of modular coordination. Tentative square footages and dimensions are developed, based on multiples of the module. As the size requirements of the spaces become apparent, a planning module is developed which guides the orderly design of the spaces and suggests materials and structural systems best suited to the final organization and coordination of the elements of the building.

A sound knowledge of building materials and structural systems is essential to the architect for an intelligent development of the preliminary plan solutions. It is during this phase that major dimensions are established and the basic construction components and plan elements are organized and related to each other and to the over-all modular grid. The grid is sometimes used visually in the preliminary stages, either ruled or printed on tracing paper or on a plastic underlay sheet. More often it is merely visualized by the architect and expressed only in terms of modular dimensions.

There is no single method of designing a building based on modular principles. The approach may vary, depending on the type of building and on the materials and structural system. The planning grid, also, may vary, taking on any shape as dictated by functional requirements, structural requirements, or the dimensional requirements of materials, components, or equipment.

Important initial decisions are made during the

2
DESIGN

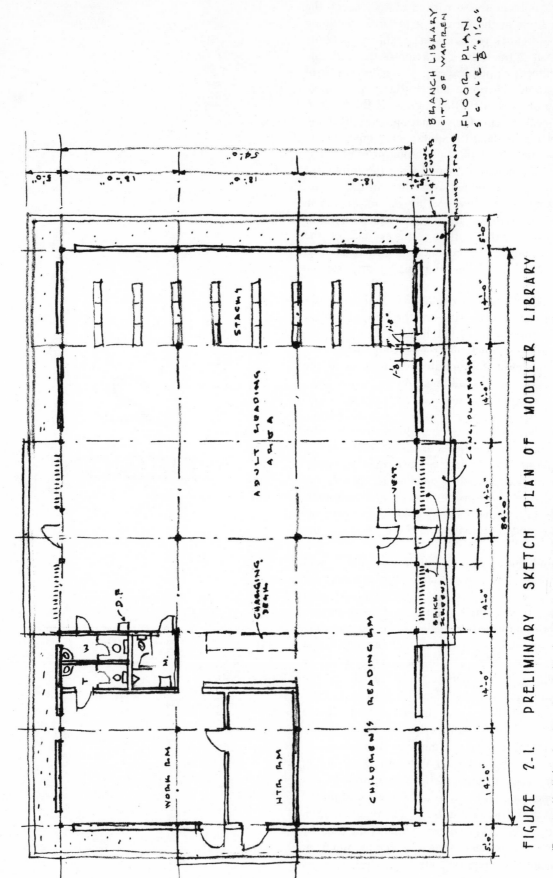

FIGURE 2-1.   PRELIMINARY SKETCH PLAN OF MODULAR LIBRARY

(Tarapata–MacMahon Associates, Inc., Architects and Engineers, Bloomfield Hills, Michigan:
Branch Library, Warren, Michigan)

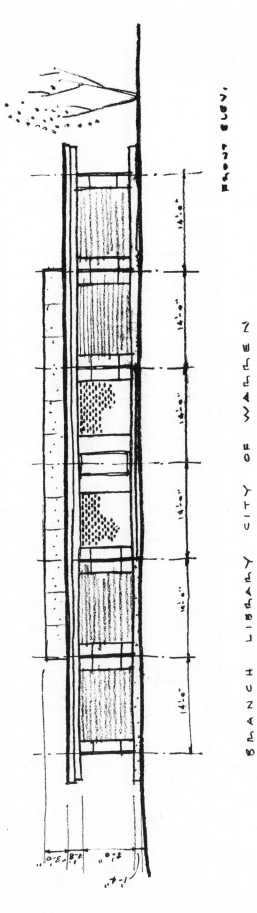

BRANCH LIBRARY CITY OF WARREN

FIGURE 2-2. PRELIMINARY SKETCH ELEVATION OF MODULAR LIBRARY

(Tarapata–MacMahon Associates, Inc., Architects and Engineers, Bloomfield Hills, Michigan:
Branch Library, Warren, Michigan)

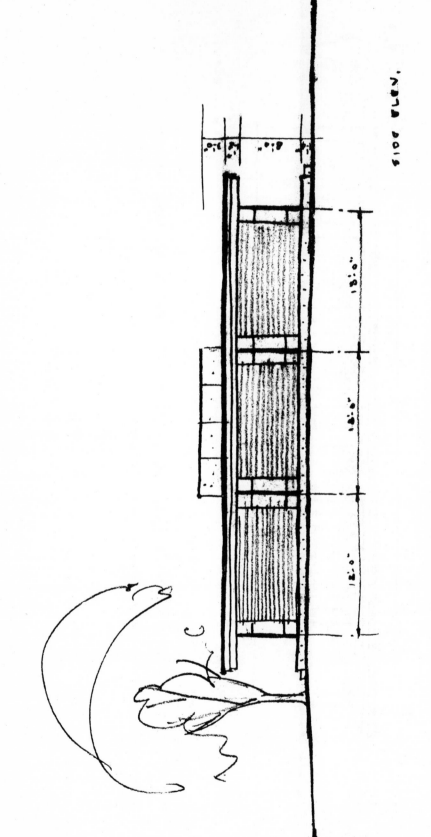

BRANCH LIBRARY CITY OF WARREN

FIGURE 2-3.   PRELIMINARY SKETCH ELEVATION
OF MODULAR LIBRARY

(Tarapata–MacMahon Associates, Inc., Architects and Engineers, Bloomfield Hills, Michigan:
Branch Library, Warren, Michigan)

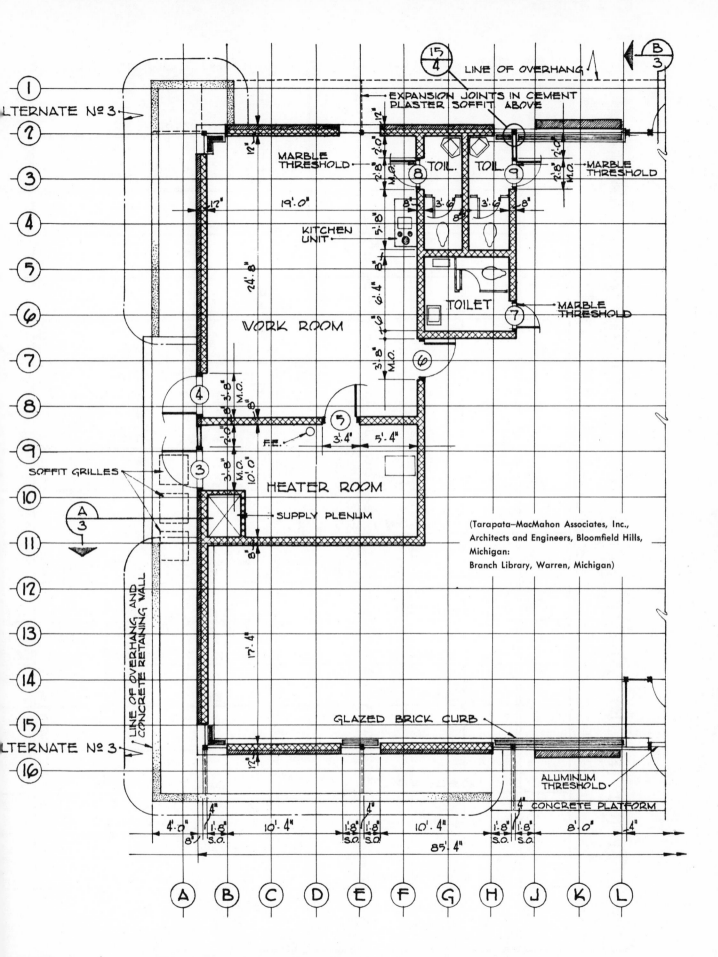

FIGURE 2-4. PORTION OF COMPLETED FLOOR PLAN, MODULAR LIBRARY

(Tarapata–MacMahon Associates, Inc., Architects and Engineers, Bloomfield Hills, Michigan: Branch Library, Warren, Michigan)

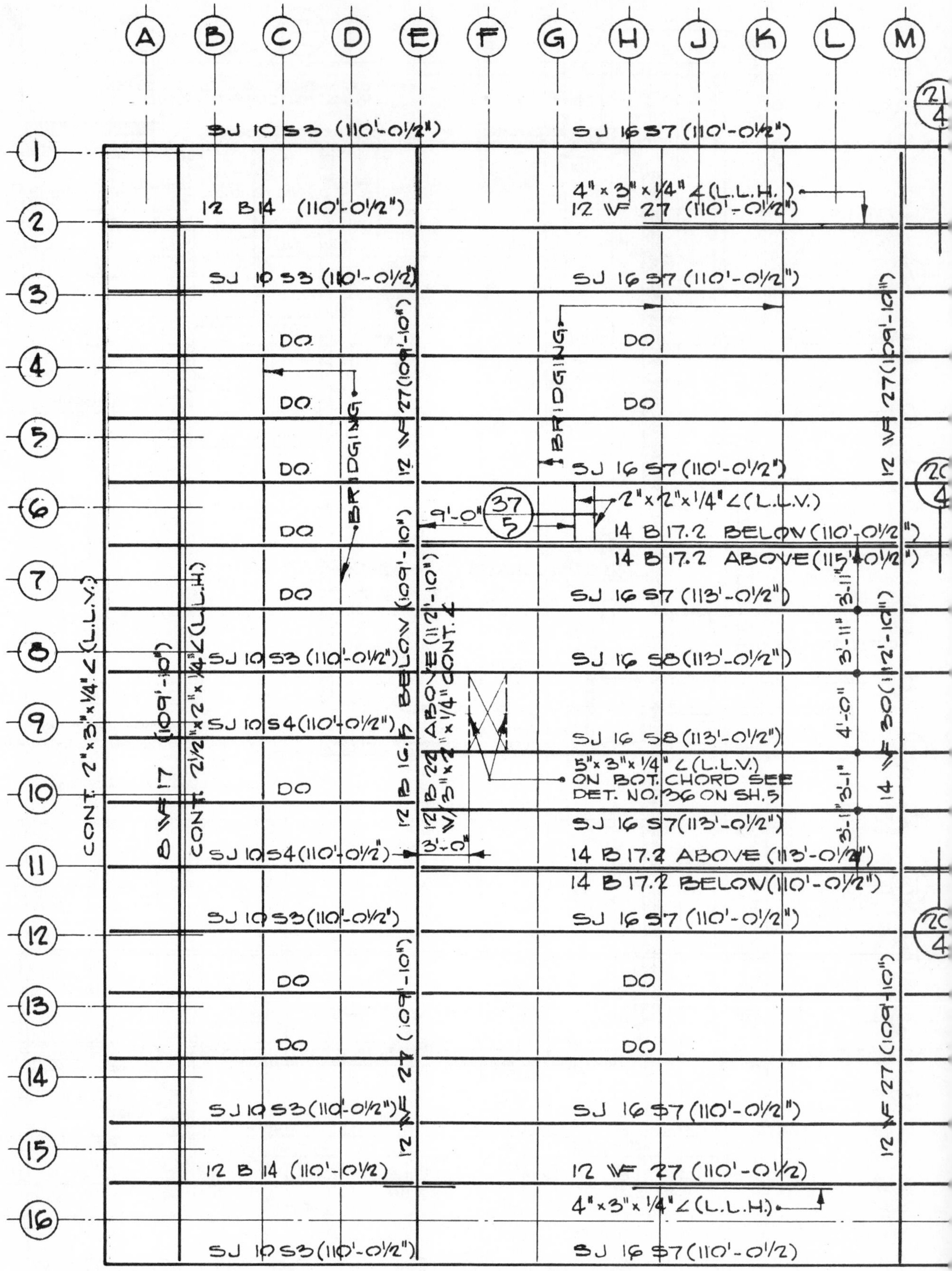

Grid columns: A B C D E F G H J K L M

SJ 10 53 (110'-0½")   SJ 16 57 (110'-0½")

12 B 14 (110'-0½")   4" x 3" x ¼" ∠ (L.L.H.)
                       12 W 27 (110'-0½")

SJ 10 53 (110'-0½")   SJ 16 37 (110'-0½")

DO   DO

DO   DO

BRIDGING   12 W 27 (109'-10")   BRIDGING   SJ 16 57 (110'-0½")

DO   2" x 2" x ¼" ∠ (L.L.V.)
      9'-0" 37/5   14 B 17.2 BELOW (110'-0½")
      14 B 17.2 ABOVE (115'-0½")

DO   SJ 16 57 (113'-0½")   3'-11"

CONT. 2" x 3" x ¼" ∠ (L.L.V.)

CONT. 2½" x 2" x ¼" ∠ (L.L.H.)   SJ 10 53 (110'-0½")   12 W 27 (112'-10") CONT. ∠   SJ 16 58 (113'-0½")   3'-11"

8 W 17 (109'-10")   SJ 10 54 (110'-0½")   14 B 16.5 BELOW (109'-10")   12 B 16.5 ABOVE (112'-10")   SJ 16 58 (113'-0½")   4'-0"   14 W 30 (112'-10")

DO   5" x 3" x ¼" ∠ (L.L.V.)
      ON BOT. CHORD SEE
      DET. NO. 36 ON SH. 5   3'-1"

3'-0"   SJ 16 57 (113'-0½")
SJ 10 54 (110'-0½")   14 B 17.2 ABOVE (113'-0½")

14 B 17.2 BELOW (110'-0½")

SJ 10 53 (110'-0½")   SJ 16 57 (110'-0½")

DO   DO   12 W 27 (109'-10")

DO   DO

SJ 10 53 (110'-0½")   SJ 16 57 (110'-0½")   12 W 27 (109'-10")

12 B 14 (110'-0½")   12 W 27 (110'-0½")

4" x 3" x ¼" ∠ (L.L.H.)

SJ 10 53 (110'-0½")   SJ 16 57 (110'-0½")

Grid rows: 1 2 3 4 5 6 7 8 9 10 11 12 13 14 15 16

Details: 21/4   20/4   20/4

FIGURE 2-5. PORTION OF ROOF FRAMING PLAN,
MODULAR LIBRARY

(Tarapata–MacMahon Associates, Inc., Architects and Engineers, Bloomfield Hills, Michigan:
Branch Library, Warren, Michigan)

22

preliminary stages concerning the mechanical and electrical requirements of a building as well as the materials, structure, and visual design aspects. Basic decisions are made as to the type of heating, ventilating, and air-conditioning systems, the location of ducts and pipes and their relationship to structure, the type of lighting fixtures and provision for their placement in relation to other equipment and to structure, and other details which are involved in the development of the final scheme. All these elements can be coordinated by the use of the modular grid. In many instances, the components themselves are manufactured with modular dimensions, which makes even simpler their integration into the final design.

The preliminary plan and two elevations of a small modular library are shown in Figures 2-1 to 2-3. In this example, taken directly from the sketches of the architect, only a few basic exterior dimensions are given, all of which are multiples of 4 inches. The structural grid is clearly established, with modular dimensions given from center to center of columns. No dimensions are given in the preliminaries for the sizes of doors and interior spaces; these were understood by the architect and his staff to be modular and were left free for final adjustment in the working drawings.

The simple modular dimensions of the preliminary drawings made the transition to the working drawings rapid and easy. A portion of the final floor plan, and the front and side elevations, are shown in Figures 2-4, 2-6, and 2-7. A few differences can be seen between the preliminary and the final drawings, but these are minor, indicating the extent to which the modular coordination of the preliminary design was carried through into the final design. One major development is the addition of a reference grid to the working-drawing plan, coinciding with some of the key points. Alternate lines from the reference grid are shown on the elevations.

The majority of the dimensions in the working drawings are multiples of the basic 4-inch module, and all but a few are nonfractional. The wall section and details in Figures 2-8 and 2-9 show that most of the dimensions are given to grid lines at nominal faces of materials. An exception is the 4-inch-square steel column in Figure 2-9. It is a full 4 inches square and is dimensioned to its actual faces.

A portion of the roof framing plan is shown in Figure 2-5. There are virtually no dimensions on this plan because the location of the major beams is indicated by the placement of bearing walls and

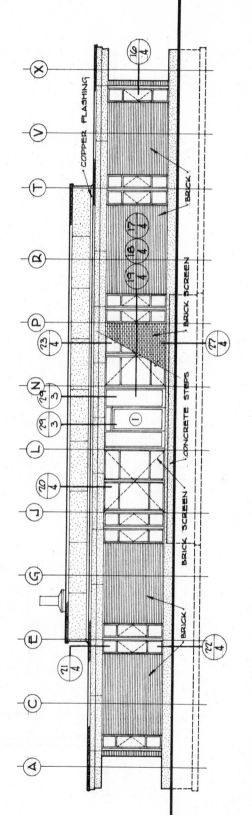

FIGURE 2-6. ELEVATION OF MODULAR LIBRARY

(Tarapata–MacMahon Associates, Inc., Architects and Engineers, Bloomfield Hills, Michigan: Branch Library, Warren, Michigan)

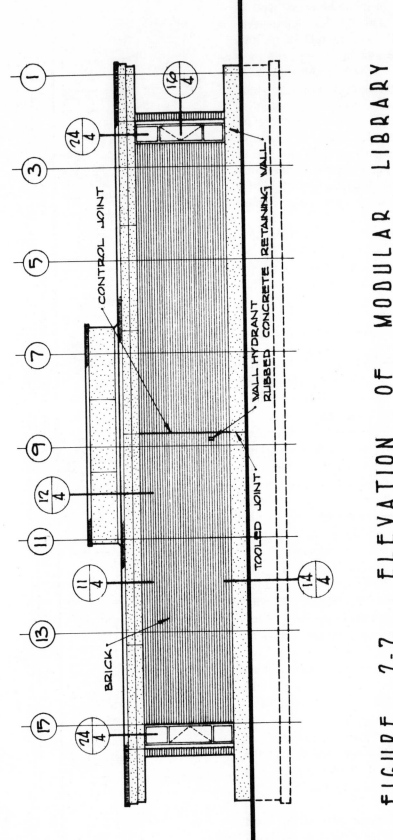

FIGURE 2-7. ELEVATION OF MODULAR LIBRARY

(Tarapata–MacMahon Associates, Inc., Architects and Engineers, Bloomfield Hills, Michigan: Branch Library, Warren, Michigan)

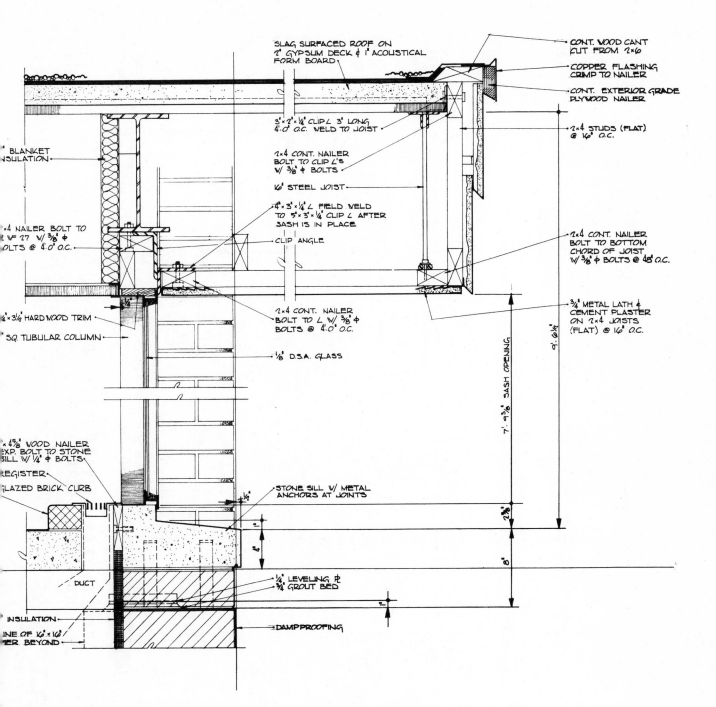

SLAG SURFACED ROOF ON
2" GYPSUM DECK & 1" ACOUSTICAL
FORM BOARD

CONT. WOOD CANT
CUT FROM 2×6

COPPER FLASHING
CRIMP TO NAILER

CONT. EXTERIOR GRADE
PLYWOOD NAILER

3"×2"×¼" CLIP ∠ 3" LONG
4'.0" O.C. WELD TO JOIST

2×4 STUDS (FLAT)
@ 16" O.C.

BLANKET
INSULATION

2×4 CONT. NAILER
BOLT TO CLIP ∠'S
W/ ⅜" ⌀ BOLTS

16" STEEL JOIST

4"×3"×¼" ∠ FIELD WELD
TO 5"×3"×¼" CLIP ∠ AFTER
SASH IS IN PLACE

2×4 NAILER BOLT TO
2 W 27 W/ ⅜" ⌀
BOLTS @ 4'.0" O.C.

CLIP ANGLE

2×4 CONT. NAILER
BOLT TO BOTTOM
CHORD OF JOIST
W/ ⅜" ⌀ BOLTS @ 48" O.C.

2×4 CONT. NAILER
BOLT TO ∠ W/ ⅜" ⌀
BOLTS @ 4'.0" O.C.

3¼" HARDWOOD TRIM

¾" METAL LATH &
CEMENT PLASTER
ON 2×4 JOISTS
(FLAT) @ 16" O.C.

SQ. TUBULAR COLUMN

⅛" D.S.A. GLASS

9'.0½"

7'.9⅝" SASH OPENING

4×4⅝" WOOD NAILER
EXP. BOLT TO STONE
SILL W/ ¼" ⌀ BOLTS

REGISTER

GLAZED BRICK CURB

STONE SILL W/ METAL
ANCHORS AT JOINTS

2⅝"

8"

DUCT

⅛" LEVELING ∤
¾" GROUT BED

INSULATION

LINE OF 16"×16"
PIER BEYOND

DAMPPROOFING

IGURE 2-8.   WALL SECTION OF MODULAR LIBRARY

(Tarapata—MacMahon Associates, Inc., Architects and Engineers, Bloomfield Hills, Michigan:
Branch Library, Warren, Michigan)

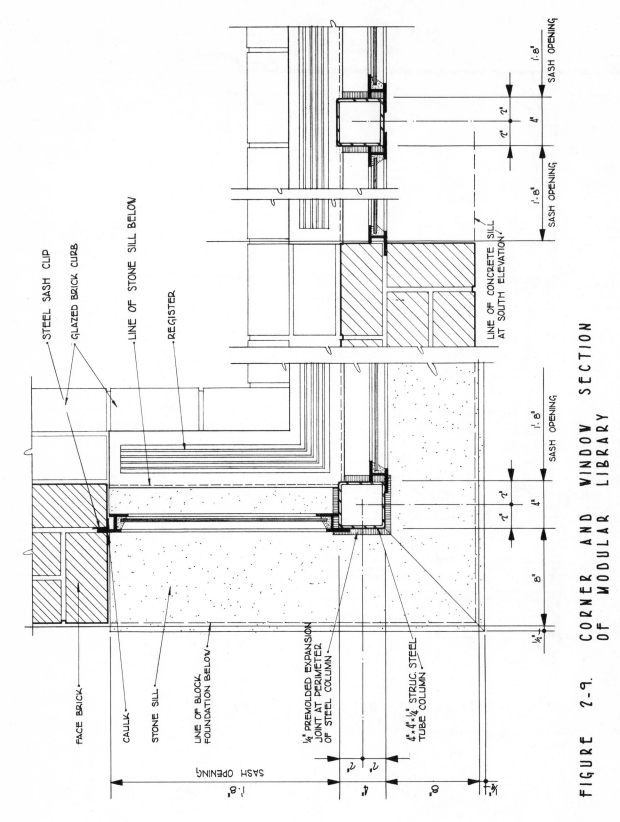

FIGURE 2-9.   CORNER AND WINDOW SECTION
OF MODULAR LIBRARY

(Tarapata–MacMahon Associates, Inc., Architects and Engineers, Bloomfield Hills, Michigan:
Branch Library, Warren, Michigan)

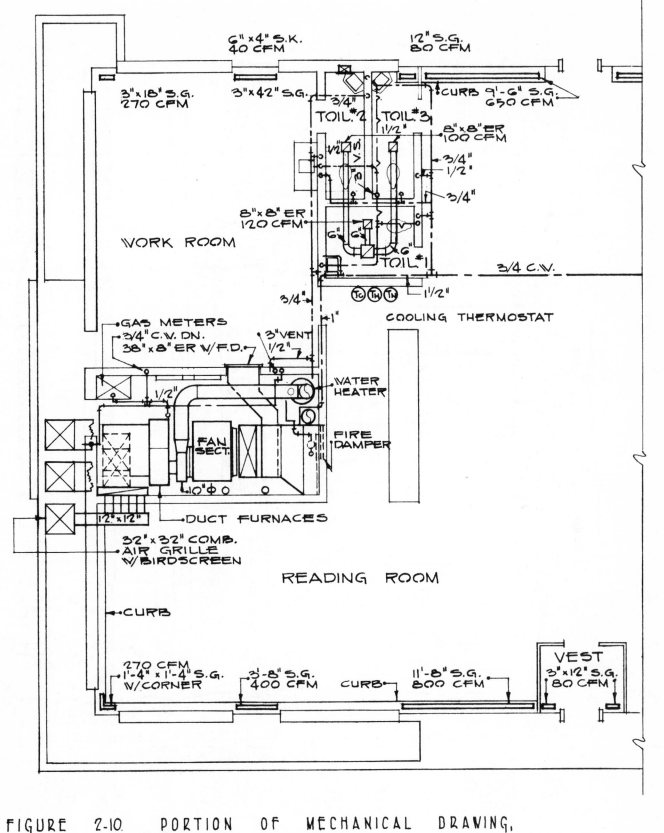

6"×4" S.K.
40 CFM

12" S.G.
80 CFM

3"×18" S.G.
270 CFM

3"×42" S.G.

3/4"

CURB 9'-6" S.G.
650 CFM

TOIL.*2 TOIL.*3

1 1/2"

8"×8" ER
100 CFM

1/2"

3/4"
1/2"

3/4"

8"×8" ER
120 CFM

WORK ROOM

6" 6"

6"

TOIL.*1

3/4 C.W.

3/4"

1 1/2"

COOLING THERMOSTAT

1"

GAS METERS
3/4" C.W. DN.
38"×8" ER W/F.D.

3"VENT
1/2"

1/2"

WATER
HEATER

FAN
SECT.

FIRE
DAMPER

10"Φ

12"×12"

DUCT FURNACES

32"×32" COMB.
AIR GRILLE
W/BIRDSCREEN

READING ROOM

CURB

270 CFM
1'-4"×1'-4" S.G.
W/CORNER

3'-8" S.G.
400 CFM

CURB

11'-8" S.G.
800 CFM

VEST

3"×12" S.G.
80 CFM

FIGURE 2-10. PORTION OF MECHANICAL DRAWING,
MODULAR LIBRARY

(Tarapata–MacMahon Associates, Inc., Architects and Engineers, Bloomfield Hills, Michigan:
Branch Library, Warren, Michigan)

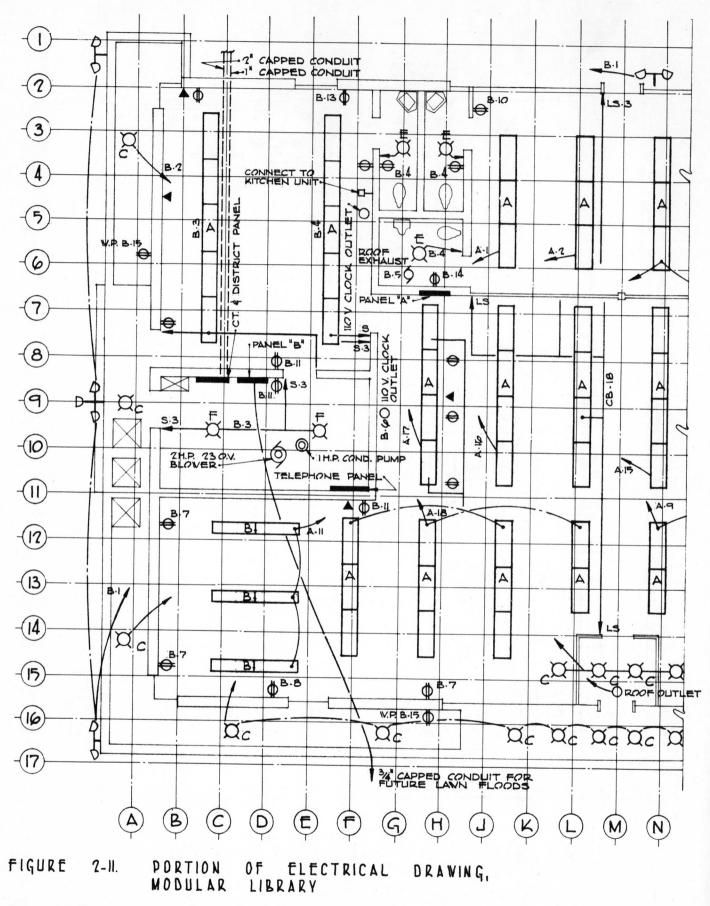

FIGURE 2-11. PORTION OF ELECTRICAL DRAWING, MODULAR LIBRARY

(Tarapata–MacMahon Associates, Inc., Architects and Engineers, Bloomfield Hills, Michigan: Branch Library, Warren, Michigan)

columns in the floor plan. The steel joists are spaced equally except where specific dimensions are given.

Portions of the mechanical and electrical layouts are shown in Figures 2-10 and 2-11. Because there is no specific relationship between the equipment shown in these drawings and the reference grid, some architects would choose to give a few precise locational dimensions as a more positive guide to the contractors.

Modular principles have been used to achieve a disciplined organization of the elements of this building without sacrificing freedom of aesthetic expression. As a result, definite benefits to the building owner in terms of clean design, accurate bidding, and more rapid construction were derived.

Wylie E. Groves High School
Birmingham, Michigan

Linn Smith Associates, Inc.
(formerly Smith-Tarapata-MacMahon)
Architects—Engineers
Birmingham, Michigan

FUNCTION OF WORKING DRAWINGS

Contract documents. Working drawings are part of the legal documents used by the building owner and the contractor selected to erect the building. These documents define the work and the terms under which it is to be done and are referred to as the *contract documents*. They usually consist of th*e contract* itself, which is signed by the owner, or his agent, and the contractor, and which establishes the responsibilities of all parties; the *written specifications*, which describe specific materials and items and the quality and workmanship of the project; and the *working drawings*, which define in visual detail the building and the site, with all necessary dimensions, materials, services, details of structure, mechanical and electrical equipn.ent, and other items necessary for a complete building.

Working drawings. Working drawings, as a visual means of communication, should be simple, clear, precise, complete, and accurate. They are used by the architect to show his final design solution, which includes the location of the building on its site, existing site conditions, the finished site, foundation plans and details, floor plans, elevations, sections, construction details, structure, mechanical and electrical equipment and layout, and colors and finishes. The presentation of this information with simplicity and clarity requires careful organization of the building design and its subsequent delineation in the working drawings.

Accurate dimensions and effective details will result only if the design concept is clear to the architect and to the draftsmen who develop the drawings. Useful working drawings have precise dimensions and are consistent in the method of dimensioning. Details, and the methods of connecting and joining materials, are shown clearly. To achieve this end, clarity in the initial coordination of parts and in their relationship to the whole structure, and an ability on the part of the architect to communicate the design concept in all its detail to his draftsmen, are required.

OFFICE PROCEDURES FOR PRODUCTION OF DRAWINGS

All architectural offices have drafting procedures which are followed by the personnel responsible for the production of the working drawings. Typical of the things which are standardized are sheet size and format, scale of drawings, material indications, and dimensioning techniques. Modular drawings, as the graphic expression of the modular thinking and the modular organization which go into the development of the design concept of a

3

DEVELOPMENT OF WORKING DRAWINGS

building, are a positive means of achieving simplicity of organization and presentation.

An effective method of using modular practice in the development of a complete and accurate set of final working drawings is the use of a small-scale dummy set of working drawings. Before the final working drawings are started, the job captain prepares a complete layout of the proposed sheets of drawings, usually at one-fourth of their actual scale. This enables him to analyze the project, determine what drawings are required and the specific sheet on which each should be located, and establish the scale of each drawing. These layout sheets, when stapled together as a book and kept on file for reference, relieve the draftsmen of the need to make decisions concerning selection of drawings, location, and scale.

Modular practice is applied to expedite the development of these sheets by using reference grids to aid in the cross-referencing of drawings. Reference lines from the modular grid are used to locate starting points for plan dimensions, to establish floor lines in elevations, and to establish specific locations of materials and components in sections and details. Finally, consistent modular-dimensioning technique in the office enables the draftsmen easily to convert the small sketches of the layout sheets into the completed working drawings of the final set.

This method promotes efficient production of modular working drawings. The principles involved in its application include an understanding of modular practice by all office personnel, agreement on the specific techniques of modular dimensioning to be utilized by an office, use of modular grid lines, reference grid lines, and structural grid lines to achieve coordination between drawings, and preplanning of the required drawings and their location in the working drawings.

COORDINATION BY MEANS OF THE GRID

The influence of modular dimensioning in coordinating plan and elevation was shown in Figure 1-3. Even though the complete modular grid is not shown, its presence is implied by the dimensions, which are all multiples of 4 inches. The reference and structural grids formalize the system and give expression to the coordination of the parts, in addition to providing a coordinate system for locating specific points on the plan. A basic datum point should be given on the site to which the grids are referred dimensionally for accurate location of the building at the beginning of construction.

CHOICE OF SCALE FOR WORKING DRAWINGS

The scale selected for a particular drawing depends on the type of information which is to be conveyed to the contractor. The scale of any drawing should be no larger than is necessary to convey the required information in readable form. This applies also to the production of engineering drawings, in which efficiency, clarity, and accuracy are extremely important. The scales discussed below are based on general usage in architectural offices. The experience of offices which use modular practice indicates that modular dimensioning can, at times, permit the choice of a smaller scale than is used for nonmodular drawings.

Plot plans and site development. The determining factors for choice of scale for plot plans usually are size of site, size of working-drawing sheet, and amount of detailed information desired.

A small scale such as $1'' = 20'0''$ is usually used for plot plans in order to include the whole site and its immediate surroundings, which may have an influence on the placement of the building and the location of services to it. The scale may be either decimal or foot-inch. The plot plan for a modular dormitory is shown in Figure 3-1. The size of the drawing is reduced here in order that the complete scope of the drawing may be shown. A portion of this plot plan is presented in Figure 3-2 at a scale only slightly reduced from the original.

Plans. The purpose of a plan drawing is to serve as a reference for basic construction layout and for location of details. At the usual scale of $\frac{1}{8}'' = 1'0''$, little information can be given concerning wall materials and details of furniture and equipment layout. Larger-scale drawings of specific plan areas are used to present more information.

Even $\frac{1}{8}$-inch-scale plan layouts of a large project, such as a campus-plan high school, are often too big to fit on one sheet. Drawings are continued from one sheet to another, and match lines are used to show the continuity. Architects prefer to get a complete floor plan on one sheet, but find it difficult to reduce the scale below $\frac{1}{8}'' = 1'0''$ because of the problems involved in fitting fractional dimensions into the small spaces of a $\frac{1}{16}'' = 1'0''$ floor plan. However, some architects who use modular dimensioning draw most of their floor plans at $\frac{1}{16}$-inch scale and provide all the dimensions and other information necessary for the contractor to lay out the job and locate all basic plan elements. These plans are used as reference drawings, and complex areas and details are singled out and referred to other sheets of the working drawings where they

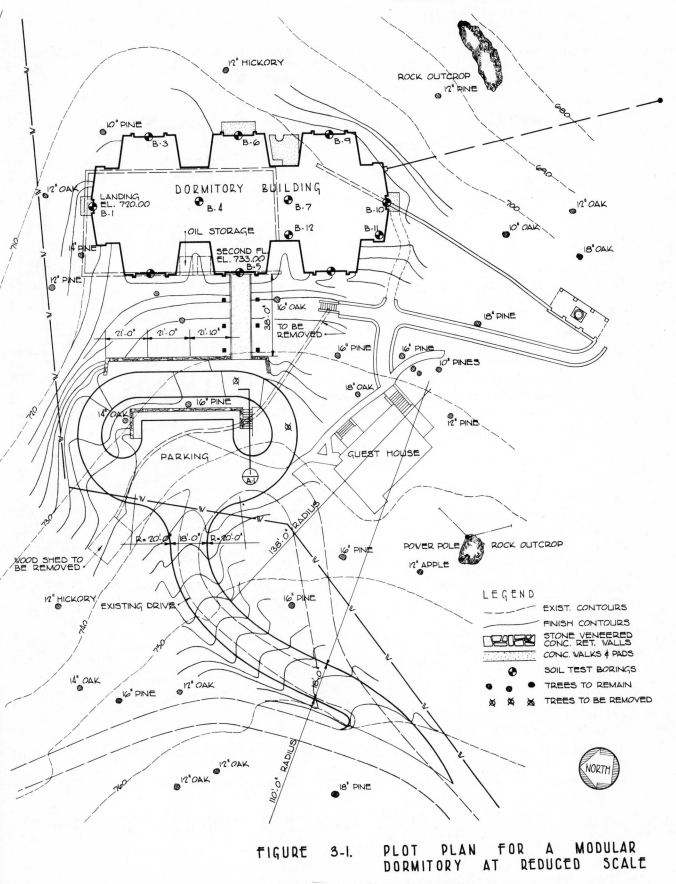

FIGURE 3-1.   PLOT PLAN FOR A MODULAR
DORMITORY AT REDUCED SCALE

(Aeck Associates, Architects, Atlanta, Georgia:

Girls' Dormitory, Tallulah Falls School, Tallulah Falls, Georgia)

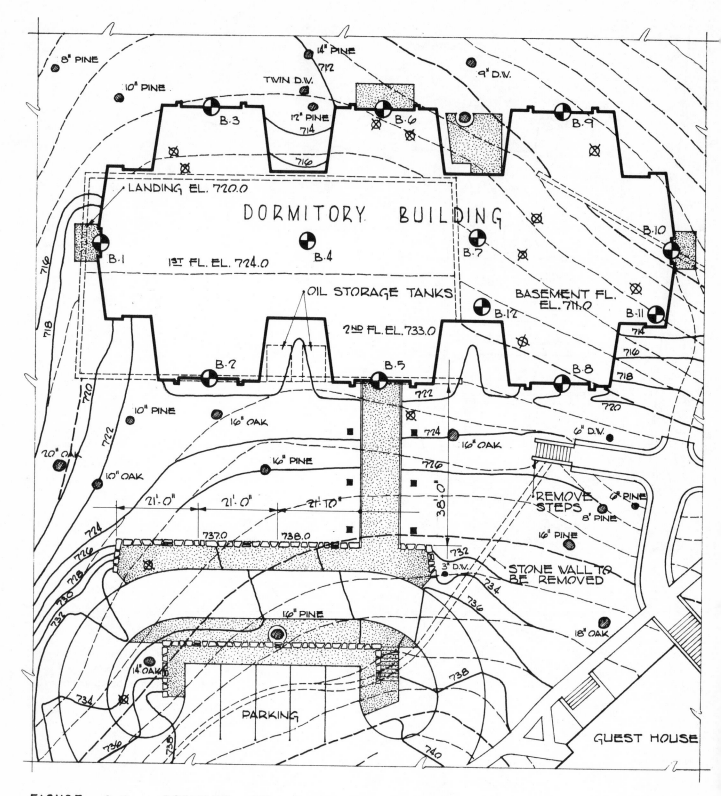

FIGURE 3-2.   PORTION OF PLOT PLAN FOR MODULAR DORMITORY
AT SLIGHTLY REDUCED SCALE

(Aeck Associates, Architects, Atlanta, Georgia:
Girls' Dormitory, Tallulah Falls School, Tallulah Falls, Georgia)

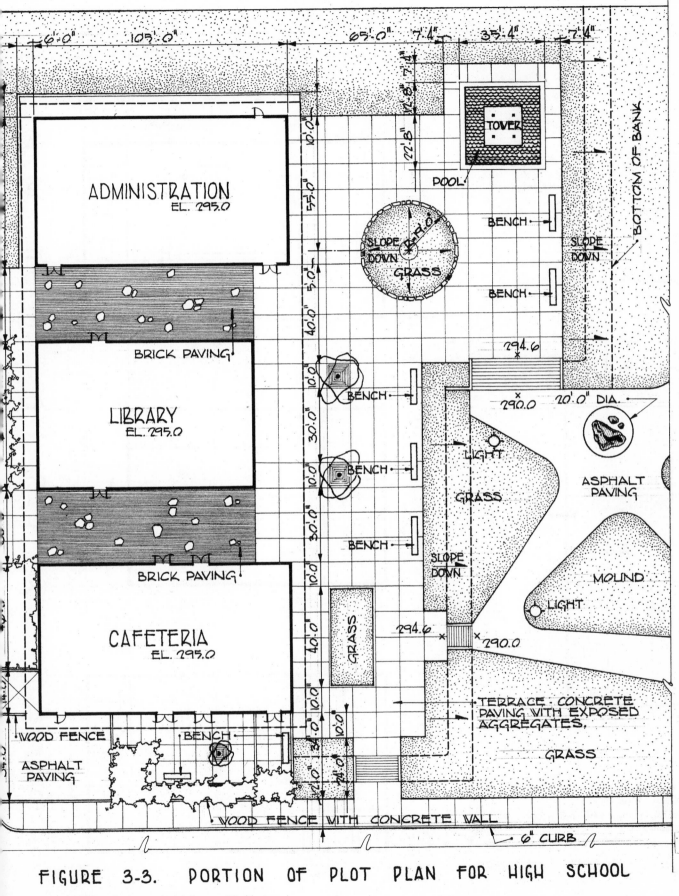

FIGURE 3-3. PORTION OF PLOT PLAN FOR HIGH SCHOOL

(Robert Billsbrough Price, Architect, Tacoma, Washington:
Mount Tahoma High School, Tacoma, Washington)

35

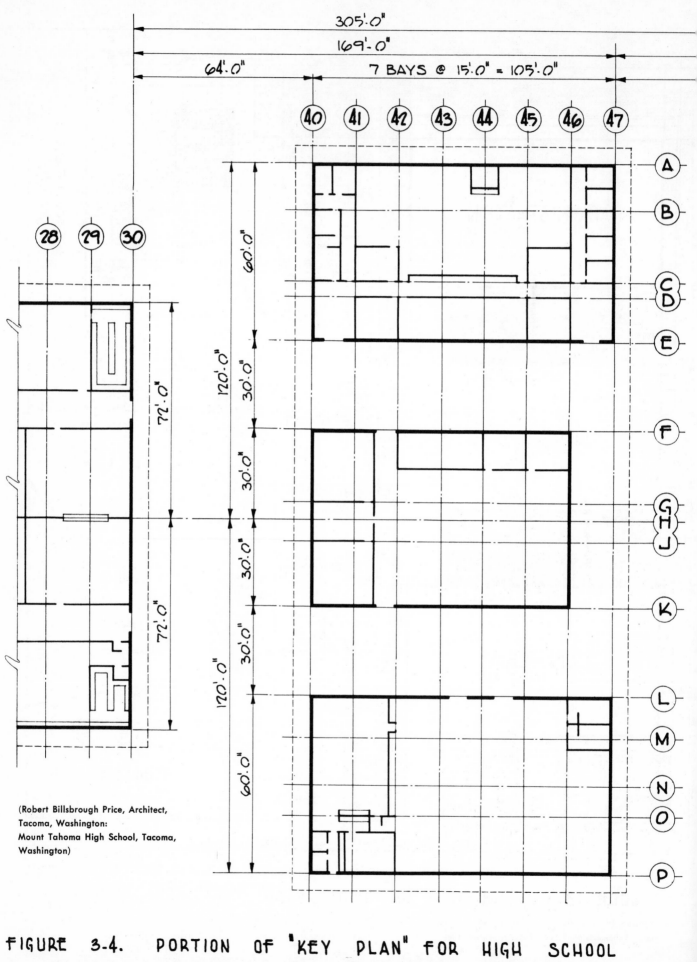

(Robert Billsbrough Price, Architect,
Tacoma, Washington:
Mount Tahoma High School, Tacoma,
Washington)

FIGURE 3-4. PORTION OF "KEY PLAN" FOR HIGH SCHOOL

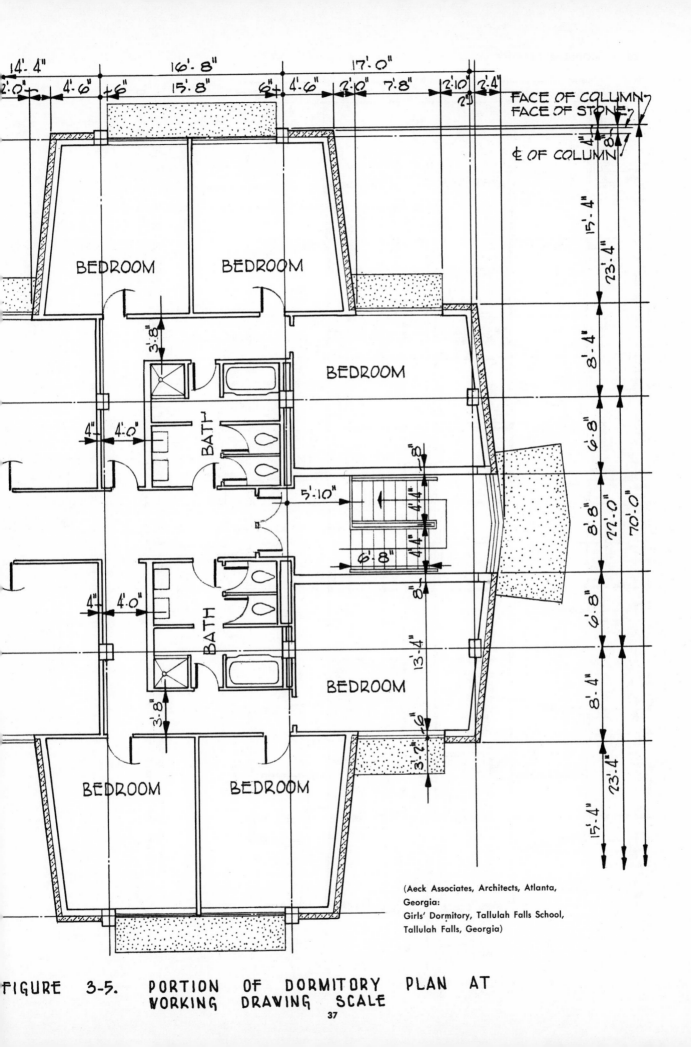

FACE OF COLUMN
FACE OF STONE
℄ OF COLUMN

BEDROOM

BEDROOM

BEDROOM

BATH

BATH

BEDROOM

BEDROOM

BEDROOM

(Aeck Associates, Architects, Atlanta, Georgia:
Girls' Dormitory, Tallulah Falls School,
Tallulah Falls, Georgia)

FIGURE 3-5. PORTION OF DORMITORY PLAN AT
WORKING DRAWING SCALE

37

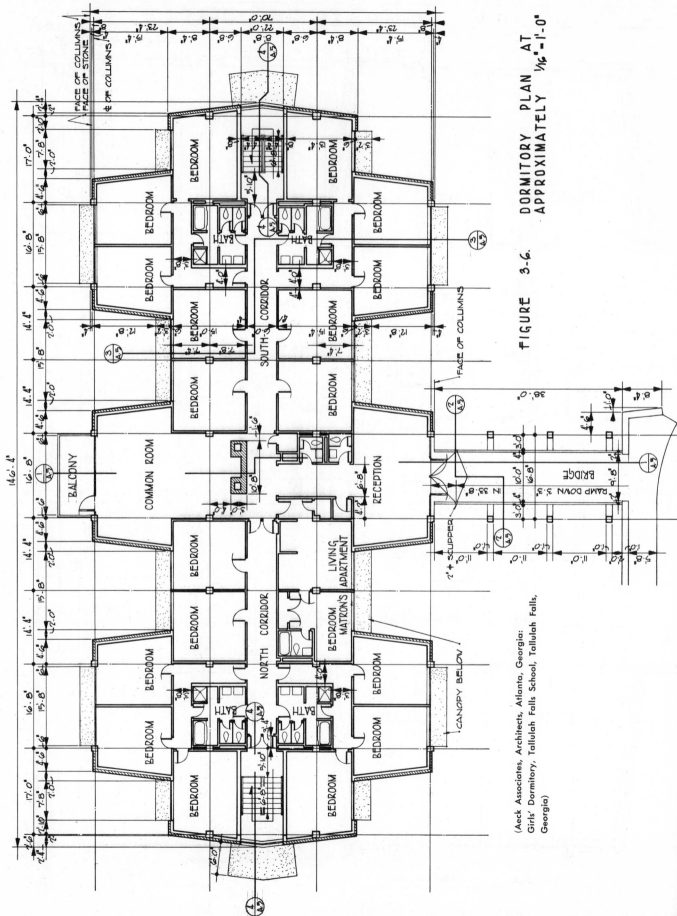

FIGURE 3-6.   DORMITORY PLAN AT
APPROXIMATELY 1/16"=1'-0"

(Aeck Associates, Architects, Atlanta, Georgia:
Girls' Dormitory, Tallulah Falls School, Tallulah Falls,
Georgia)

are presented at larger scale, just as they are for ⅛-inch plans.

In unusually large jobs, where even 1/16-inch drawings will not fit on one sheet, an even smaller scale such as ½₂″ = 1′0″ is used. These drawings are normally labeled "master plan," "key plan," or "diagrammatic plan." Complete with major exterior dimensions, reference and structural grids, and single-line indication of interior walls and partitions, they give the contractor a picture of the whole scheme and the relationship and size of its elements. The actual working-drawing plans are still drawn at the smallest scale consistent with clarity and accuracy, whether it is 1/16, ⅛, or ¼ inch, and are drawn on as many sheets as are required. Portions of the plot plan and the corresponding "key plan" of a high school are shown in Figures 3-3 and 3-4.

In Figure 3-5, a portion of the plan of the dormitory shown in the plot plan in Figures 3-1 and 3-2 is given at the scale used by the architect in his working drawings, ⅛″ = 1′0″. The complete plan, redrawn at 1/16″ = 1′0″, is shown in Figure 3-6, and in Figure 3-7 it is drawn at ½₂″ = 1′0″ as a "key plan." Each of these progressively smaller scales requires more simplicity than the next larger one. The contribution of modular dimensioning to a successful reduction of scale can be seen in Figure 3-6. Without this approach, this plan would be difficult to draw clearly if fractional dimensions were involved.

Elevations. Elevations are drawn at the same scale as plans so that they may be more easily drawn and coordinated with the plans. Specific parts which should be shown in more detail are enlarged in separate drawings. Reference or structural grid lines which are shown in plan are also shown on the elevations to aid visual coordination between the two. Dimensions between the reference or structural grid lines are not shown on the elevation drawings.

Horizontal grid lines which refer to specific construction elements are shown on elevations. Frequently, only floor lines are shown, with actual datum-point elevations given as well as the floor-to-floor heights. Occasionally, vertical dimensions are given to other features of the elevations, such as window sills and heads. These are kept to a minimum because they are shown in wall section and detail drawings, and duplication can lead to errors and loss of time.

The north and east elevations of the dormitory in Figures 3-8 and 3-9 are drawn at two different scales for illustrative purposes. The scale of ⅛″ = 1′0″ in Figure 3-8 is the one most commonly used for elevations. It is large enough to show materials and other pertinent information, and it is also the scale most often used for floor plans. When the plans are reduced in scale, the elevations are drawn at the smaller scale also, as in Figure 3-9.

In Figures 3-8 and 3-9, the structural grid is also a reference grid. This makes the orientation of the elevations with the plans accurate and easy to follow. An interesting point to note in this project is the use of dots in the plans (Figures 3-5 and 3-6) to indicate the modular spacing of the columns along the east and west sides. Even though the spacings are modular, the dots are used because the

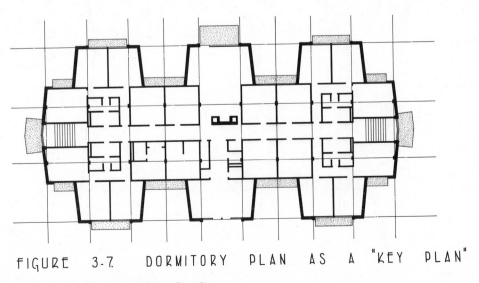

FIGURE 3-7. DORMITORY PLAN AS A "KEY PLAN"

(Aeck Associates, Architects, Atlanta, Georgia:
Girls' Dormitory, Tallulah Falls School, Tallulah Falls, Georgia)

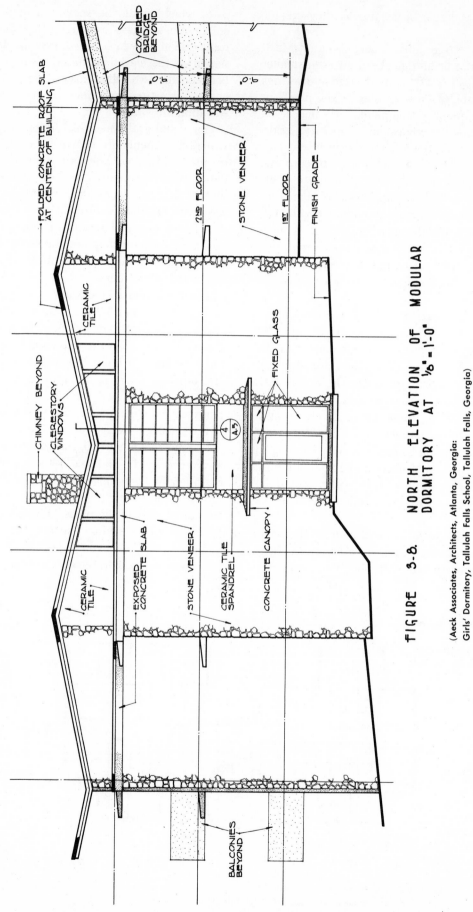

FIGURE 3-8. NORTH ELEVATION OF MODULAR DORMITORY AT ⅛" = 1'-0"

(Aeck Associates, Architects, Atlanta, Georgia:
Girls' Dormitory, Tallulah Falls School, Tallulah Falls, Georgia)

Labels within figure:
COVERED BRIDGE BEYOND
FOLDED CONCRETE ROOF SLAB AT CENTER OF BUILDING
2ND FLOOR
STONE VENEER
1ST FLOOR
FINISH GRADE
CERAMIC TILE
CHIMNEY BEYOND
CLERESTORY WINDOWS
FIXED GLASS
CERAMIC TILE
EXPOSED CONCRETE SLAB
STONE VENEER
CERAMIC TILE SPANDREL
CONCRETE CANOPY
BALCONIES BEYOND
9'-0"
9'-0"

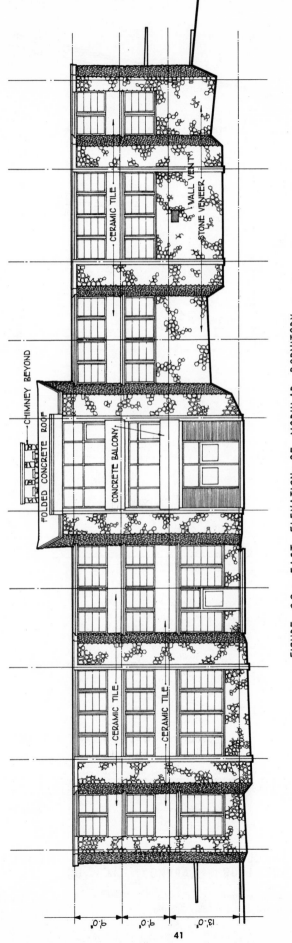

FIGURE 3.9. EAST ELEVATION OF MODULAR DORMITORY
AT $1/16" = 1'-0"$

(Aeck Associates, Architects, Atlanta, Georgia:
Girls' Dormitory, Tallulah Falls School, Tallulah Falls, Georgia)

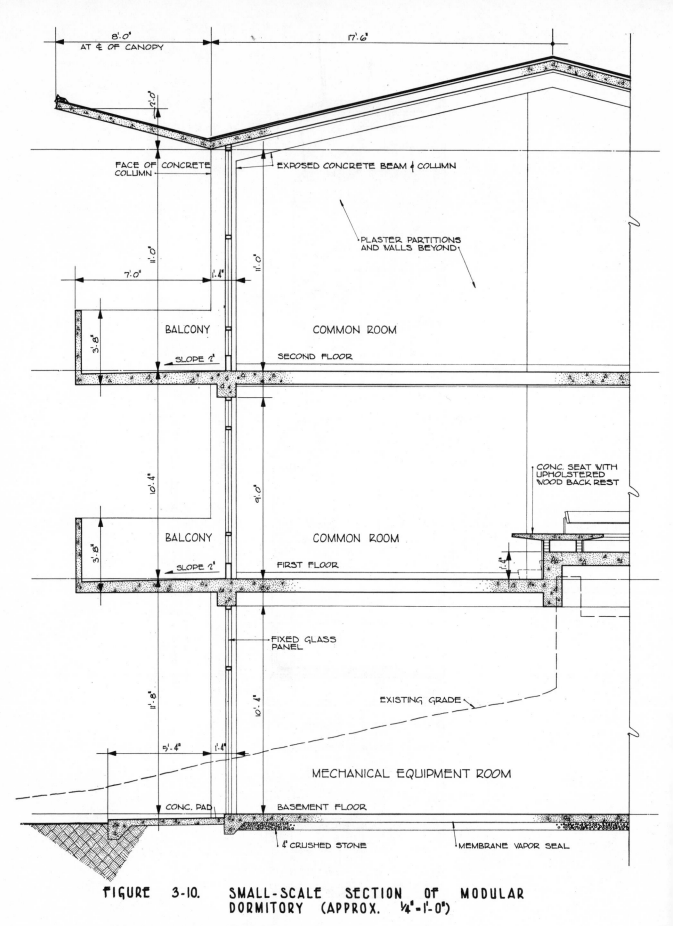

FIGURE 3-10. SMALL-SCALE SECTION OF MODULAR DORMITORY (APPROX. ¼"-1'-0")

(Aeck Associates, Architects, Atlanta, Georgia:
Girls' Dormitory, Tallulah Falls School, Tallulah Falls, Georgia)

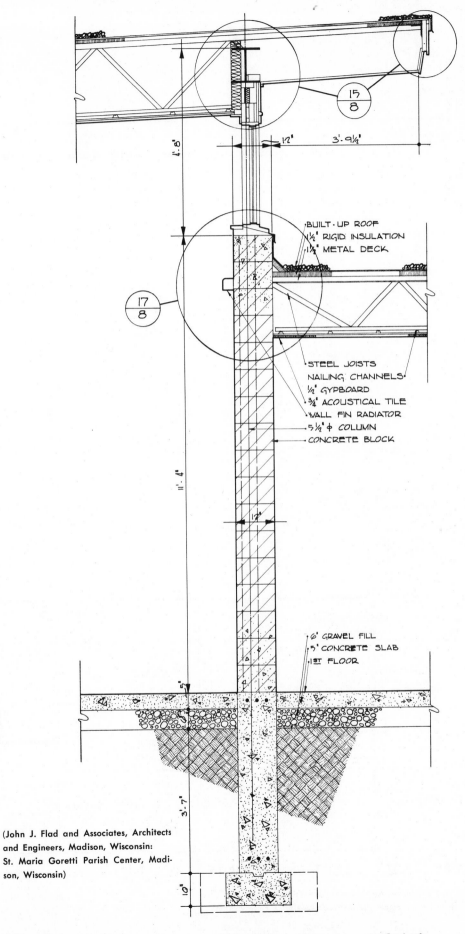

BUILT-UP ROOF
1½" RIGID INSULATION
1½" METAL DECK

STEEL JOISTS
NAILING CHANNELS
½" GYPBOARD
¾" ACOUSTICAL TILE
WALL FIN RADIATOR
5½" ∅ COLUMN
CONCRETE BLOCK

6" GRAVEL FILL
5" CONCRETE SLAB
1ST FLOOR

(John J. Flad and Associates, Architects
and Engineers, Madison, Wisconsin:
St. Maria Goretti Parish Center, Madison, Wisconsin)

FIGURE 3-11. WALL SECTION (APPROX. ½"- 1'-0")

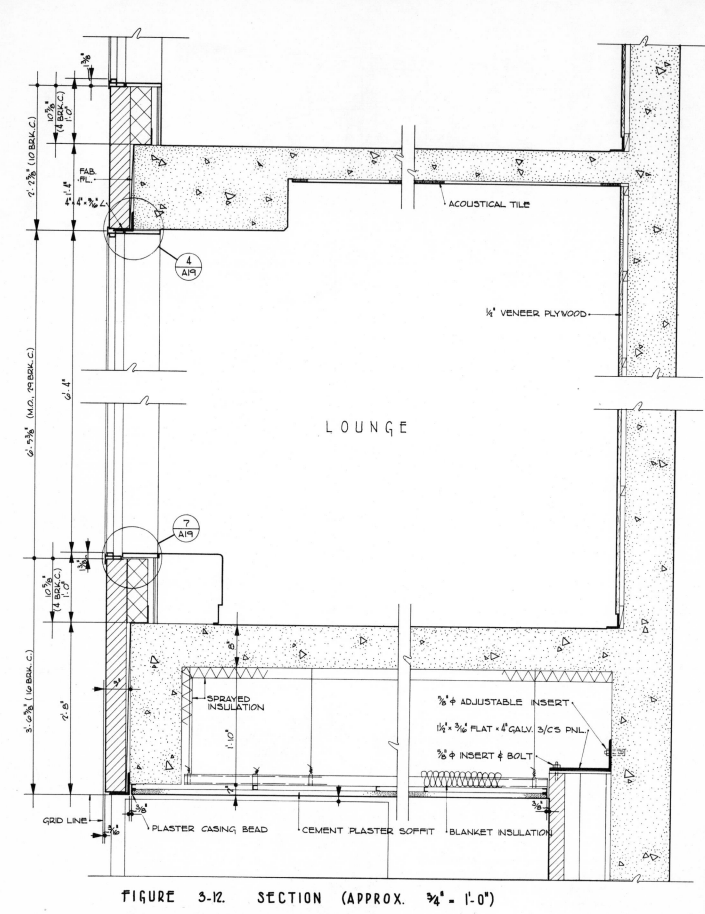

LOUNGE

ACOUSTICAL TILE

½" VENEER PLYWOOD

SPRAYED INSULATION

⅝" φ ADJUSTABLE INSERT

1½" × 3/16" FLAT × 4" GALV. 3/CS PNL.

⅝" φ INSERT & BOLT

GRID LINE

PLASTER CASING BEAD — CEMENT PLASTER SOFFIT — BLANKET INSULATION

FIGURE 3-12. SECTION (APPROX. ¾" = 1'-0")

(Nolen and Swinburne, Architects, Philadelphia, Pennsylvania:
Men's Dormitories, Temple University, Philadelphia, Pennsylvania)

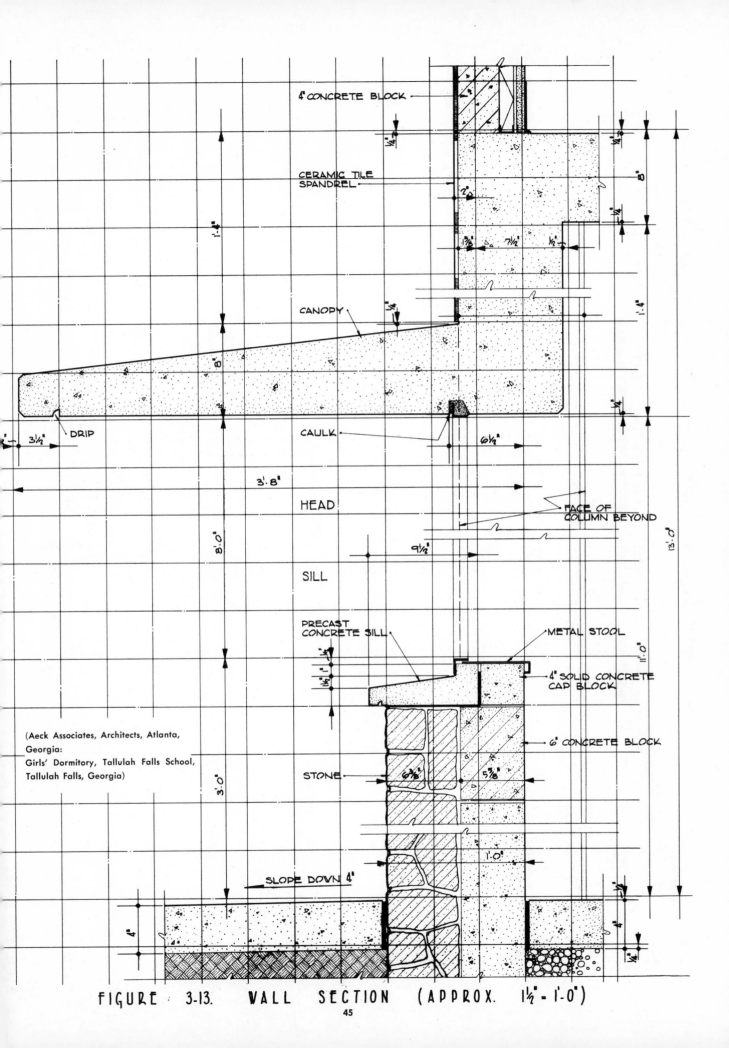

4" CONCRETE BLOCK

CERAMIC TILE
SPANDREL

CANOPY

DRIP

3½"

3'-8"

HEAD

SILL

PRECAST
CONCRETE SILL

STONE

SLOPE DOWN 4"

CAULK

FACE OF
COLUMN BEYOND

9½"

6½"

METAL STOOL

4" SOLID CONCRETE
CAP BLOCK

6" CONCRETE BLOCK

(Aeck Associates, Architects, Atlanta,
Georgia:
Girls' Dormitory, Tallulah Falls School,
Tallulah Falls, Georgia)

FIGURE 3-13. WALL SECTION (APPROX. 1½" = 1'-0")

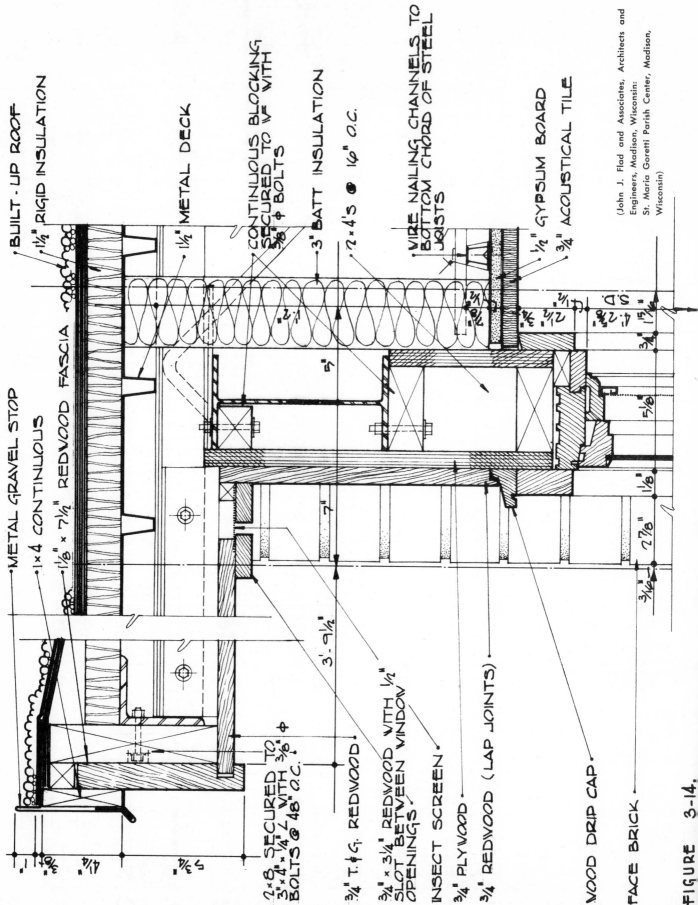

- BUILT-UP ROOF
- 1½" RIGID INSULATION
- METAL DECK
- CONTINUOUS BLOCKING SECURED TO W F WITH ⅜" Ø BOLTS
- 3" BATT INSULATION
- 2"×4's @ 16" O.C.
- WIRE NAILING CHANNELS TO BOTTOM CHORD OF STEEL JOISTS
- ½" GYPSUM BOARD
- ¾" ACOUSTICAL TILE

(John J. Flad and Associates, Architects and Engineers, Madison, Wisconsin: St. Maria Goretti Parish Center, Madison, Wisconsin)

- METAL GRAVEL STOP
- 1×4 CONTINUOUS
- 1⅛" × 7½" REDWOOD FASCIA

- 2×8. SECURED TO 3"×4"×¼" L WITH ⅜" Ø BOLTS @ 48" O.C.
- ¾" T.&G. REDWOOD
- ¾" × ¾" REDWOOD WITH ½" SLOT BETWEEN WINDOW OPENINGS
- INSECT SCREEN
- ¾" PLYWOOD
- ¾" REDWOOD (LAP JOINTS)

- WOOD DRIP CAP
- FACE BRICK

FIGURE 3-14.

column center lines are not on modular grid lines. A nonmodular dimension of 2 feet 6 inches at each end of the building establishes the off-grid centering of the columns.

Sections. The scale of sections through a building or through portions of it is influenced not so much by complex dimensions and extensive notes as by the type of visual information required. Complete sections which are cut through a whole building are often drawn at the same scale as the plan merely to show structural and spatial relationships. If the size of the drawing at this scale is too small to be of value, it is doubled. Vertical modular dimensions are given to important points in these small sections, and the specific relationships between dimensions and construction are defined in larger-scale sections and in large-scale details. An example of a small-scale building section is shown

in Figure 3-10, which is drawn at $\frac{1}{4}'' = 1'0''$, twice the scale of the original floor plans.

Wall sections at $\frac{1}{2}'' = 1'0''$, $\frac{3}{4}'' = 1'0''$ and $1\frac{1}{2}'' = 1'0''$ are used to show construction relationships in the enclosing elements of a building. The larger scales are often preferred because they allow more precision in indicating materials and the points to which dimensions are taken. On the other hand, because these larger scales require more space on the sheet, the scale of $\frac{1}{2}'' = 1'0''$ is used when more of the vertical height of a building must be included in one drawing. Simple, nonfractional modular dimensions fit more easily into the smaller-scale sections than do complex fractional dimensions and may influence the choice of scale.

Wall sections from two projects are given in Figures 3-11 and 3-12, the first at $\frac{1}{2}'' = 1'0''$ and the

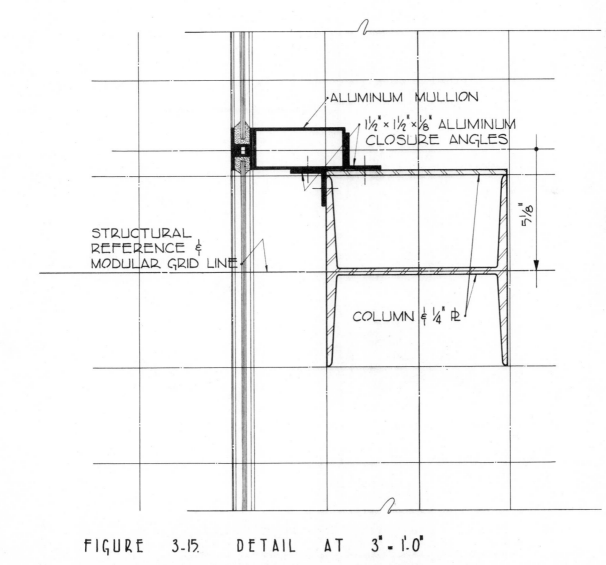

FIGURE 3-15.   DETAIL   AT   3" = 1'-0"

(Pederson, Hueber and Hares, Architects; Glavin, Landscape Architect, Syracuse, New York:
Westhill Junior-Senior High School, Onondaga County, New York)

second at ¾″ = 1′0″. A wall section for the dormitory shown in this chapter is shown in Figure 3-13 at 1½″ = 1′0″, the scale used by the architect for all wall sections in the working drawings for this project. These sections served also as detail drawings, and separate details of the same areas at a larger scale were not required. Taken together, these three wall-section illustrations show the capabilities and limitations of the different scales. In each one, proper use of the modular grid and modular dimensions results in clarity and simplicity and aids in coordinating the section with the plan and elevation drawings.

Details. Large-scale architectural details in working drawings are used to show the specific relationships between materials. They indicate the precise sizes and shapes desired by the architect, as well as the required methods of fastening and connecting the parts. Modular dimensioning can influence the choice of scale of details. Although the scale of 3″ = 1′0″, which is one-fourth full size, is used for many details, 1½″ = 1′0″ is preferred frequently for combination wall section/details because it is large enough to include the information usually shown in 3-inch details, and also small enough to include the large area generally shown by a ¾-inch wall section. The use of this scale is made possible by the simplification and coordination provided by modular dimensioning. Half-size and full-size details are used when the architect wants to be precise about the shape of a part or about a method of connection.

The use of the modular grid in details can be helpful in locating the exact points to which meas-

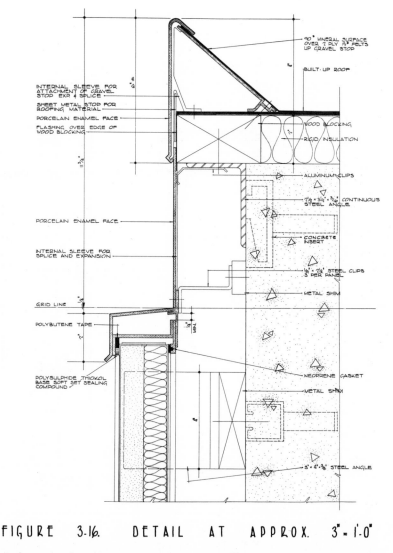

FIGURE 3-16.   DETAIL AT APPROX. 3″=1′-0″

(Perkins and Will, Architects–Engineers, White Plains, New York, and Washington, D. C.:
International Minerals and Chemical Corporation Offices, Skokie, Illinois)

urements are taken and in relating details to the structure as a whole. It is necessary to show only a minimum number of grid lines to establish the relationship between a detail and the whole modular grid.

Details at scales of $3'' = 1'0''$ and one-half full size, from several different projects, are shown in Figures 3-14 to 3-18. The immediate coordination with the floor plan through modular dimensioning and the reference grid can be seen clearly in Figure 3-15, in which the grid line through the center of the steel column is part of the structural and reference grids, which are shown on the plans and elevations, and is also part of the over-all modular grid.

Modular grid lines are used to help develop details at an early stage in the design of a building. Modular dimensions are shown on all preliminary plans to establish the modular concept, and tentative details of corners, mullions, column connections, and other specific points are worked out on the grid for early coordination.

Structural, mechanical, and electrical drawings. Some types of drawings, such as those prepared by the mechanical engineer, may include information too complex to be shown with a scale as small as $\frac{1}{16}'' = 1'0''$. The scale should be selected to suit the requirements of a particular project. Generally, it is more convenient for the engineer to work directly from the architectural drawings, at the same scale.

Examples of engineering drawings at $\frac{1}{8}'' = 1'0''$ are given in Figures 3-19 and 3-20. The first is a structural plan, and the other a mechanical plan. The architectural plans for this modular project were drawn at $\frac{1}{8}'' = 1'0''$, and the engineering

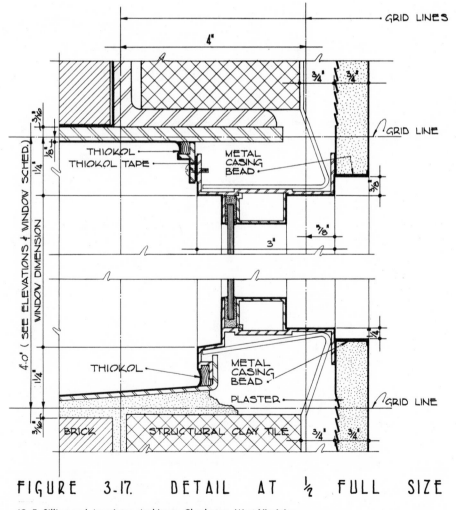

FIGURE 3-17.   DETAIL AT ½ FULL SIZE

(C. E. Silling and Associates, Architects, Charleston, West Virginia: West Virginia University Medical Center Housing, Morgantown, West Virginia)

drawings were based on them. Conceivably, both the architectural and the engineering drawings could have been drawn at $\frac{1}{16}'' = 1'0''$. A portion of the structural plan for a large hospital drawn at

$\frac{1}{16}'' = 1'0''$ is shown in Figure 3-21. The architectural plans and elevations were drawn at this scale, and the structural engineers, accustomed to working closely with the architect, used the same scale.

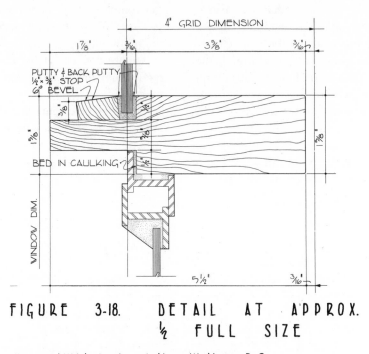

FIGURE   3-18.   DETAIL   AT   APPROX.
$\frac{1}{2}$ FULL   SIZE

(Brown and Wright Associates, Architects, Washington, D. C.:
Bogounoff Residence, Langley, Virginia)

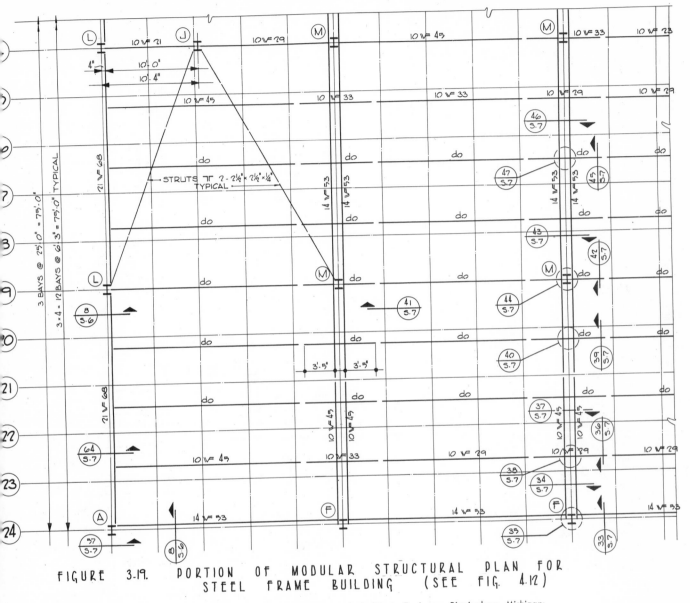

FIGURE 3.19.   PORTION OF MODULAR STRUCTURAL PLAN FOR
STEEL FRAME BUILDING (SEE FIG. 4.12)

(Linn Smith Associates, Inc. (formerly Smith-Tarapata-MacMahon, Inc.), Architects–Engineers, Birmingham, Michigan:
Flint School District Administration Building, Flint, Michigan)

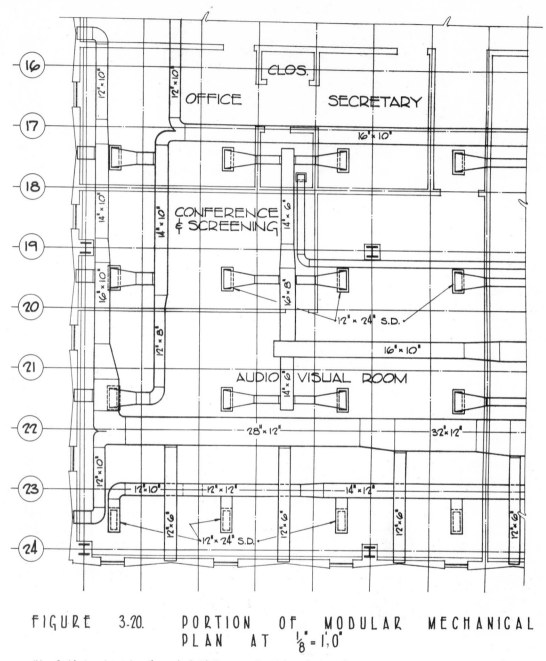

FIGURE   3·20.   PORTION   OF   MODULAR   MECHANICAL
PLAN   AT $\frac{1}{8}" = 1'·0"$

(Linn Smith Associates, Inc. (formerly Smith-Tarapata-MacMahon, Inc.), Architects–Engineers, Birmingham, Michigan:
Flint School District Administration Building, Flint, Michigan)

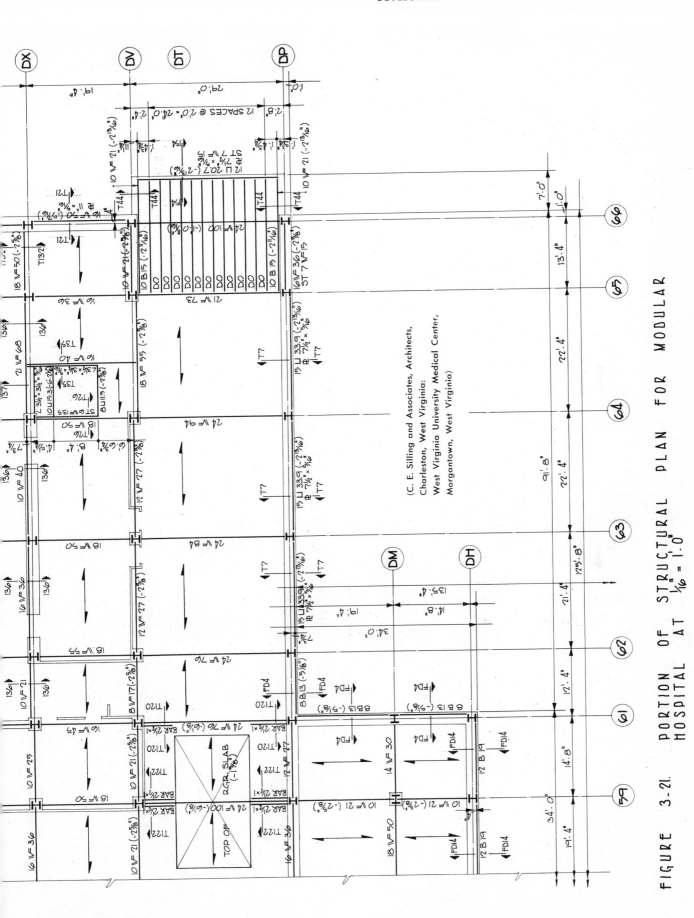

FIGURE 3-21. PORTION OF STRUCTURAL PLAN FOR MODULAR HOSPITAL AT $\frac{1}{16}" = 1'.0"$

(C. E. Silling and Associates, Architects, Charleston, West Virginia: West Virginia University Medical Center, Morgantown, West Virginia)

Lovett School
Atlanta, Georgia

Aeck Associates
Architects
Atlanta, Georgia

FUNCTION OF PLANS

Plan drawings are the means by which the architect conveys to the contractor all the information concerning plan arrangement, dimensions, and location of materials which he needs for bidding, layout, and construction. They contain references to larger-scale drawings of construction features and specific plan areas which the architect wishes to show in more detail.

A plan drawing should be simple, precise, and uncluttered. Excessive notes and material indications should be eliminated, as well as complicated and unnecessary dimensions. Modular practice aids considerably in the simplification of plans and often results in the reduction of the scale of the plan drawings.

The application of modular dimensioning in plans to building dimensions, columns, doors and windows, and partitions is discussed in the following sections.

BUILDING DIMENSIONS

The use of over-all dimensions on the exterior of floor plans is shown in Figures 4-1, 4-2, 4-9, and 4-12. All these dimensions are multiples of 4 inches and were developed during the early design of the buildings. The modular concept was used as the coordinating principle. Not all the required dimensions are shown in these drawings, but the simple end-to-end dimensions are subdivided to indicate major divisions in the exteriors of the buildings. From these few dimensions, the contractor can lay out the basic form of the building. A positive starting point which locates the building and its modular grid with respect to a datum point on the site should be indicated clearly on the plans.

Traditionally, modular dimensioning has been associated most frequently with masonry construction. Now, however, it is applied to all types of construction. Variations in the details from one type to another sometimes require a slightly different application of the modular grid at the exterior wall line. Although the principles of modular dimensioning as applied to details are given in Chapter 6, the exterior-wall conditions which affect major dimensions are presented in this chapter.

Masonry. The standard modular brick is manufactured to measure 8 inches in length when combined with one mortar joint. A 4-inch grid superimposed on this brick and joint falls on the center line of the joint at each end of the brick. If a grid line were placed directly on one end of the brick, confusion would result, with the grid line at one end of the building falling one full joint width be-

4
PLANS

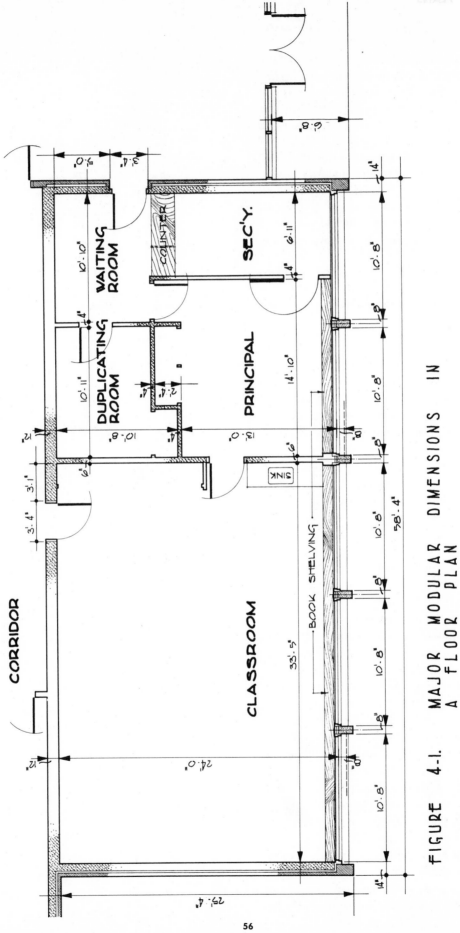

FIGURE 4-1. MAJOR MODULAR DIMENSIONS IN A FLOOR PLAN

(Vine and Robinson, Architects, Toronto and Brampton, Ontario, Canada: Regency Acres Public School, Aurora, Ontario, Canada)

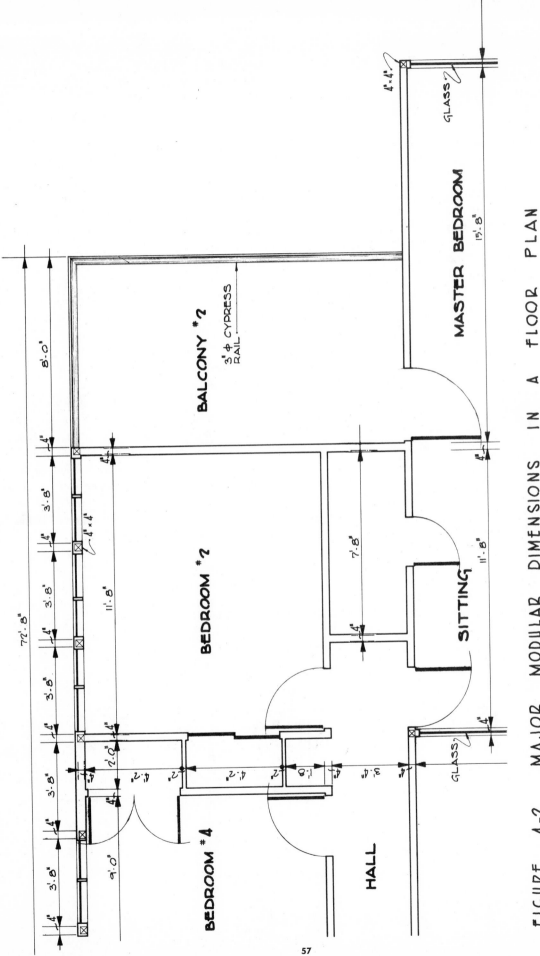

FIGURE 4-2. MAJOR MODULAR DIMENSIONS IN A FLOOR PLAN

(Brown and Wright Associates, Architects, Washington, D. C.: Bogounoff Residence, Langley, Virginia)

yond the last brick, and at the other end of the building, at the actual face of the brick. The normal relationship of modular bricks to the 4-inch grid is shown in Figure 4-3.

Modular bricks are usually manufactured to use a ⅜-inch mortar joint, with a half joint of ³⁄₁₆ inch. The location of the grid lines at an exterior corner of a brick wall and in the corresponding wall section is shown in Figure 4-4. The grid is ³⁄₁₆ inch beyond the face of the brick to allow the grid lines along the wall to fall at the center of the joints. This is a standard convention for modular masonry. In laying out the building, the contractor makes the actual dimension one full joint shorter than the modular dimension shown on the drawings, and the masons lay the brick in line with the face of the foundation wall. Some contractors mark both the modular grid line and the actual building line on the batter boards and use the modular line to establish permanent reference check points inside the building before the batter boards are lost. A number of these reference locations may be established to correspond with specific locations on the drawings, such as column center lines. When the building has been started, the check points and the modular grid help the workmen to place the materials accurately.

Variations in which the brick projects beyond the face of the foundation wall or is recessed back from it are treated by maintaining the grid at the half-joint location with relation to the brick, and dimensioning from the last grid line to the actual foundation face.

Other materials or components, regardless of size, which are separated by joints, are dimensioned in the same manner as bricks, with the grid lines located at the joint center lines. The illustrations in this section are intended only as examples of the principles of modular dimensioning. A completed set of working-drawing plans will have more dimensions than the plans in Figures 4-1, 4-2, 4-9, and 4-12. Also, a corner detail such as that in Figure 4-4 will not show the dimensions of individual bricks, nor will it necessarily show the complete grid. Only the exterior grid line is required to establish the point to which dimensions are given.

Developed working-drawing floor plans are shown at the end of this chapter, with the influence of construction type and reference grid reflected in the final dimensions.

Wood frame. Wood-frame construction varies from one section of the country to another. These variations make it difficult to establish one single method of handling exterior-wall details and overall building dimensions. As in masonry construction, a few simple conventions are followed and are called to the attention of the contractor with a note on the first sheet of drawings.

Two standard ways of placing an exterior stud wall on a foundation wall are shown in Figures 4-5 and 4-6. In both cases the studs in the exterior wall are centered between the lines of the 4-inch grid. However, in Figure 4-5 the studs are set back from the foundation wall by the thickness of the sheathing, in this case ¾ inch, whereas in Figure 4-6 the studs are flush with the foundation wall. This difference in the placement of the exterior wall changes the relationship of the grid to the foundation wall and affects the over-all size of the building. The end-to-end dimension in Figure 4-6 is determined in the same way as the dimension for a modular brick wall, as a multiple of 4 inches with

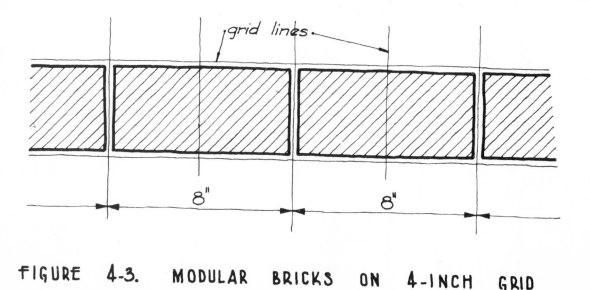

FIGURE 4-3.   MODULAR BRICKS ON 4-INCH GRID

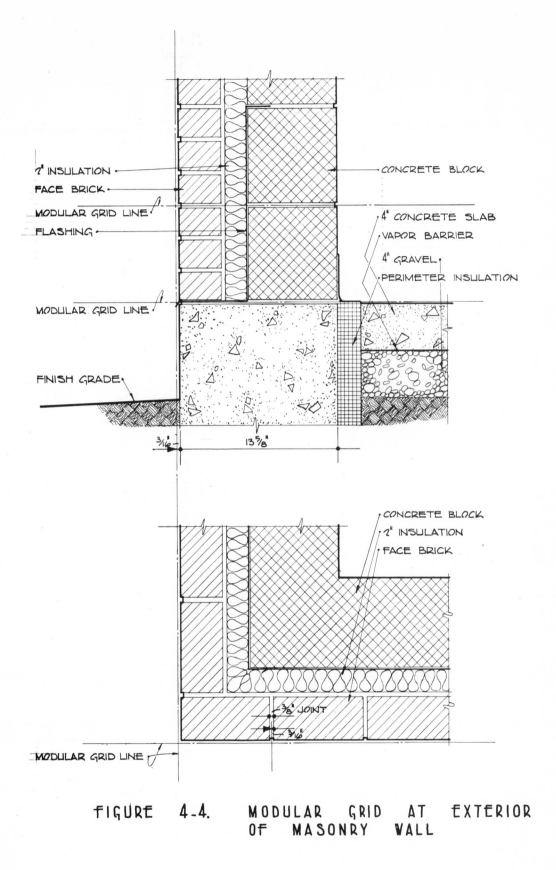

2" INSULATION
FACE BRICK
MODULAR GRID LINE
FLASHING

CONCRETE BLOCK

4" CONCRETE SLAB
VAPOR BARRIER
4" GRAVEL
PERIMETER INSULATION

MODULAR GRID LINE

FINISH GRADE

$\frac{3}{16}''$ $13\frac{5}{8}''$

CONCRETE BLOCK
2" INSULATION
FACE BRICK

$\frac{3}{8}''$ JOINT

$\frac{3}{16}''$

MODULAR GRID LINE

FIGURE 4-4. MODULAR GRID AT EXTERIOR
OF MASONRY WALL

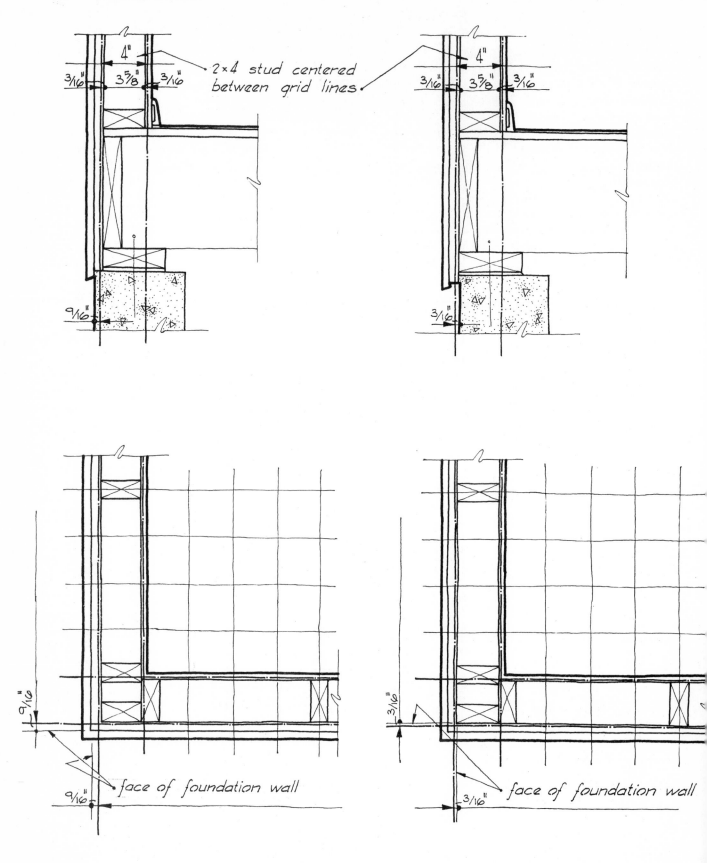

2×4 stud centered
between grid lines

4"
3/16"   3 5/8"   3/16"
9/16"

4"
3/16"   3 5/8"   3/16"
3/16"

9/16"
face of foundation wall
9/16"

3/16"
face of foundation wall
3/16"

FIGURE 4-5.   SHEATHING FLUSH
WITH FOUNDATION WALL

FIGURE 4-6.   STUDS FLUSH
WITH FOUNDATION WALL

$\frac{3}{16}$ inch less at each end for a layout dimension.

In Figure 4-5, the actual location of the foundation wall is determined by showing a $\frac{9}{16}$-inch dimension from the last grid to the face of the foundation wall. This amount at each end adds up to a total dimension $1\frac{1}{8}$ inches *longer* than the grid dimension. This relationship for the whole project is established with a note and sketch on the first sheet of working drawings, and the specific condition for foundation layout is shown on the wall sections and the foundation plan, with a simple overall actual dimension on the latter.

It is most important in using modular dimensioning to establish the grid as a **reference** *system for the three-dimensional elements of the plan and structure. No part of a plan should be forced to fall on the grid, nor should any dimensions be forced to be multiples of 4 inches.*

In both Figure 4-5 and Figure 4-6 the foundation wall is located with relation to the grid, and the exterior studs are centered between grid lines. Interior dimensions will then be modular if the interior 4-inch partitions are also centered between grid lines. This is important for efficient use of modular sheet materials as interior finish, such as wallboard and plywood. Variations in construction, such as the use of $\frac{1}{4}$-inch or $\frac{3}{8}$-inch sheathing, instead of $\frac{3}{4}$-inch sheathing, applied flush with the foundation wall, affect the relationship of the exterior stud wall to the foundation only. In the floor plan itself, the relationship of the grid to the exterior and interior walls remains unchanged.

These variations in wood-frame construction emphasize the point that modular dimensioning is not simply a matter of applying a 4-inch grid to the working drawings, but requires modular thinking at all stages of a project. As an example, the construction shown in Figure 4-5 is not as adaptable to modular dimensioning as that in Figure 4-6. The extra $1\frac{1}{8}$ inches which must be added to the overall modular dimension to establish the actual length of the foundation wall make the foundation non-modular. Modular block foundation walls would not fit this dimension, nor would modular forms for concrete foundation walls.

In Figure 4-6, the sheathing is beyond the foundation wall and, therefore, beyond the last grid line. The face of the foundation wall and the face of the stud wall on it have the same relationship to the modular grid and are unaffected in this relationship by the thickness of the sheathing.

Concrete frame. In reinforced-concrete framing, it is desirable for the framing members to relate directly to the modular grid. This is done by cen-

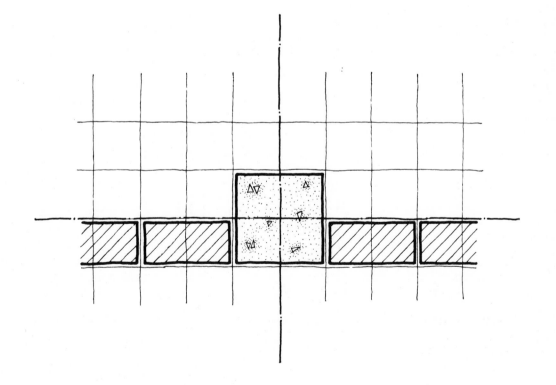

FIGURE 4-7.   CONRETE COLUMN CENTERED
ON A GRID LINE

tering the concrete columns on a grid line, as in Figure 4-7, or by centering them between grid lines if the column size is convenient, as in Figure 4-8. No effort should be made to distort the shape or size of a member unreasonably to force it to a modular size.

The exterior framing members of one simple type of concrete building are left exposed, and brick and other building materials are used as non-load-bearing fillers. In this type of building, the grid lines relate to both the frame and the masonry just as they do in a masonry building. The first grid line is located one-half joint width beyond the face, and from there the grid is used consistently throughout the building. A desirable column-masonry modular relationship is shown in Figure 4-7. The grid lines fall at the nominal column face and on column center lines. This is possible only when the column width is a multiple of 8 inches, making the half-column width a multiple of 4 inches.

Modular dimensioning applied to a specific reinforced-concrete project is shown in Figures 4-9, 4-10, and 4-11. The columns are set back from the foundation line, the window line projects beyond the foundation line, and the end wall is outside the last row of columns. The modular grid and the column grid coincide at column center lines and form a combined reference-structural grid. The major over-all dimension is given to center lines of the last row of columns at each end, as a multiple of the modular column spacing of 18′0″. The final dimension to the brick end wall is nonmodular.

This structure is a good demonstration of the concept of modular dimensioning as a *reference system* which is used to locate the major building elements and to coordinate the materials.

Steel frame. The application of modular dimensioning to a steel-frame structure is shown in Figures 4-12, 4-13, and 4-14. The structural grid of 25′0″ is subdivided into five equal parts to form a 5′0″ reference grid which is a multiple of the 4-inch modular grid. The dimensions given here indicate only the total number of reference grids and their combined dimension. The center line of the outside row of columns in both directions coincides with the nominal face of the foundation wall, thus coordinating all dimensions through the use of the modular grid. The longitudinal column center line serves as the main dimensioning reference line for final detailing of the exterior wall.

STRUCTURAL ELEMENTS

Concrete and steel columns. Structural elements such as concrete or steel columns are basic reference points. Because they are placed early and must be placed accurately, the dimensions which locate them must be clear and precise. This can be accomplished through the coordination of structural grid, reference grid, and modular grid as shown in Figures 4-9 and 4-12. Column center lines are the specific lines of coordination of all these grids. This coordination was not accomplished by application of the modular grid after the buildings were designed.

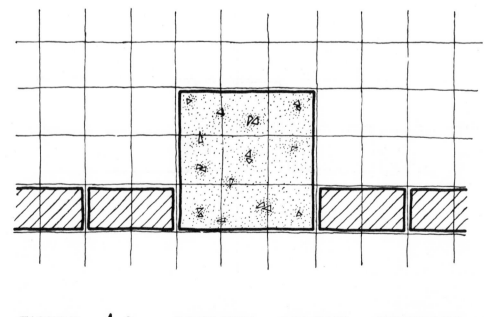

FIGURE 4-8.   CONRETE COLUMN CENTERED BETWEEN GRID LINES

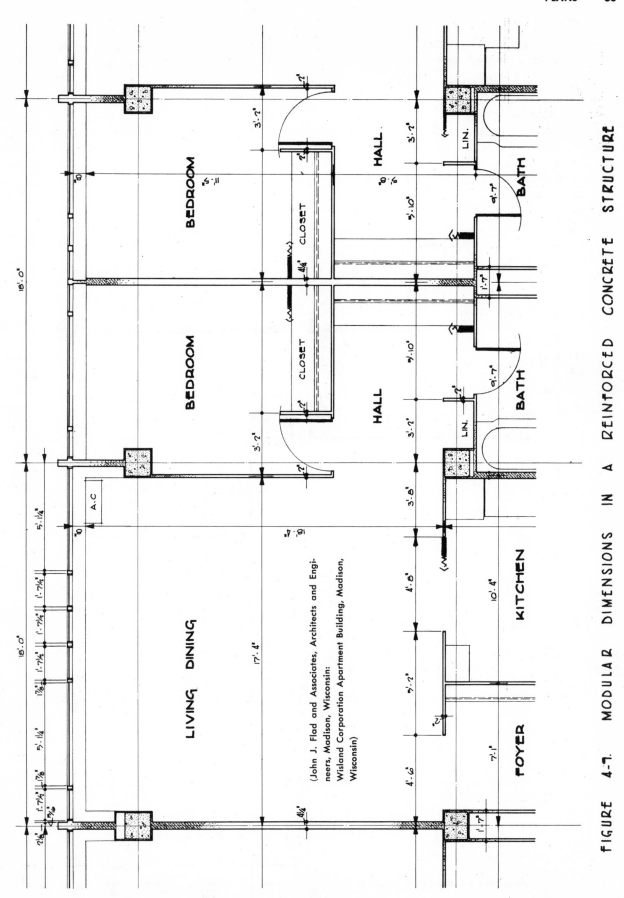

(John J. Flad and Associates, Architects and Engineers, Madison, Wisconsin: Wisland Corporation Apartment Building, Madison, Wisconsin)

FIGURE 4-7. MODULAR DIMENSIONS IN A REINFORCED CONCRETE STRUCTURE

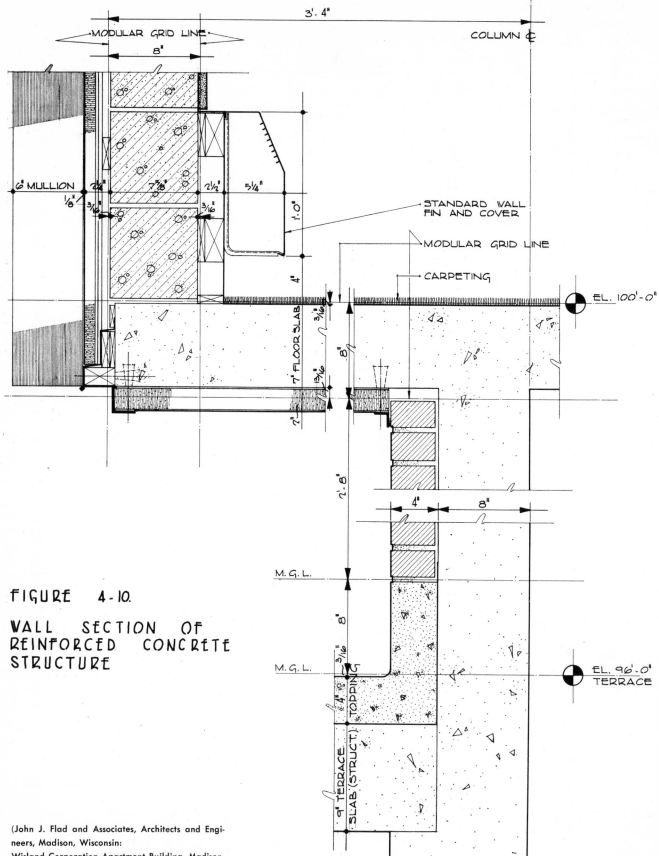

FIGURE 4-10.

WALL SECTION OF REINFORCED CONCRETE STRUCTURE

(John J. Flad and Associates, Architects and Engineers, Madison, Wisconsin:
Wisland Corporation Apartment Building, Madison, Wisconsin)

Each one was developed from its inception with the idea of modular coordination as an integrating force, and the details of each were determined at an early stage to ensure the ultimate coordination of all the parts.

"Thinking modular" from the beginning is stressed here because of its importance in the sizing of structural elements, particularly columns. When columns are in the same plane as the exterior wall, complete coordination is possible only when all materials or components, and the columns, are multiples of the module. This requirement has a tendency to lead the architect into forcing columns to a modular size. When minor adjustments in size will permit this, the ultimate savings in labor and materials will often more than compensate for any inefficiencies in use of materials. But when the change in size is unrealistic, other solutions are more appropriate. Less difficulty will be encountered in the modular sizing of columns, however, if the architect has a clear concept, from the start, of the coordination toward which he is striving.

The difficulties caused by nonmodular columns are avoided in the buildings in Figures 4-9 and 4-12

by setting the columns back from the exterior wall line. This is shown in detail in Figures 4-10, 4-11, 4-13, and 4-14. The structural grid is modular in both buildings, but the columns themselves do not need to be modular as the wall is located outside them, in a different plane. The value of this approach is seen in the steel-frame building, Figures 4-12 to 4-14, in which the fireproofed steel columns are not modular. On the other hand, the concrete-frame building, Figures 4-9 to 4-11, has columns which are multiples of 4 inches even though they are not in the wall plane.

In each of these projects, the structural, reference, and modular grids coincide with the center lines of the columns. This is standard practice in many offices and is necessary when the columns are not modular. In cases where the columns are modular, and are in the wall plane, it is effective to give the modular dimensions of the columns on the plans and details to show precisely the relationship between the columns and the modular materials which adjoin them. A portion of a modular plan, with its accompanying elevation and a column detail, is shown in Figure 4-15.

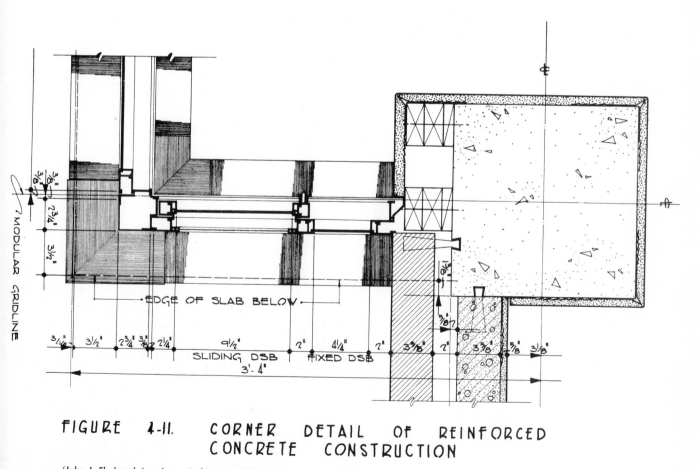

FIGURE 4-11.   CORNER DETAIL OF REINFORCED CONCRETE CONSTRUCTION

(John J. Flad and Associates, Architects and Engineers, Madison, Wisconsin: Wisland Corporation Apartment Building, Madison, Wisconsin)

Buildings in which expansion joints are used through the whole structure require a special modular-dimensioning technique. Each portion of the building between joints is treated as an individual structure and is designed and dimensioned as a modular structure complete within itself. The over-all dimension is greater than the sum of the individual buildings by the size of the total number of expansion joints. Even though the over-all dimension may be nonmodular, the economies developed by the modular coordination in the separate portions of the building more than outweigh the disadvantages of the small amount of nonmodular construction.

Modular practice has been applied successfully to a number of curvilinear buildings. In some cases a rectangular grid is used in plan as a reference system for locating the curved lines of the building passing through it. In other cases, modular units are located on the circumference of a circle for a

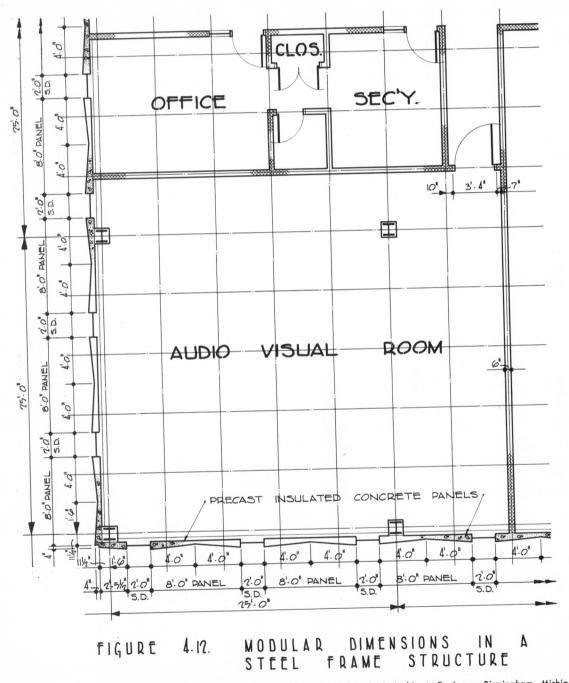

FIGURE 4.12.   MODULAR DIMENSIONS IN A
STEEL FRAME STRUCTURE

(Linn Smith Associates, Inc. (formerly Smith–Tarapata–MacMahon, Inc.), Architects–Engineers, Birmingham, Michigan; Flint School District Administration Building, Flint, Michigan)

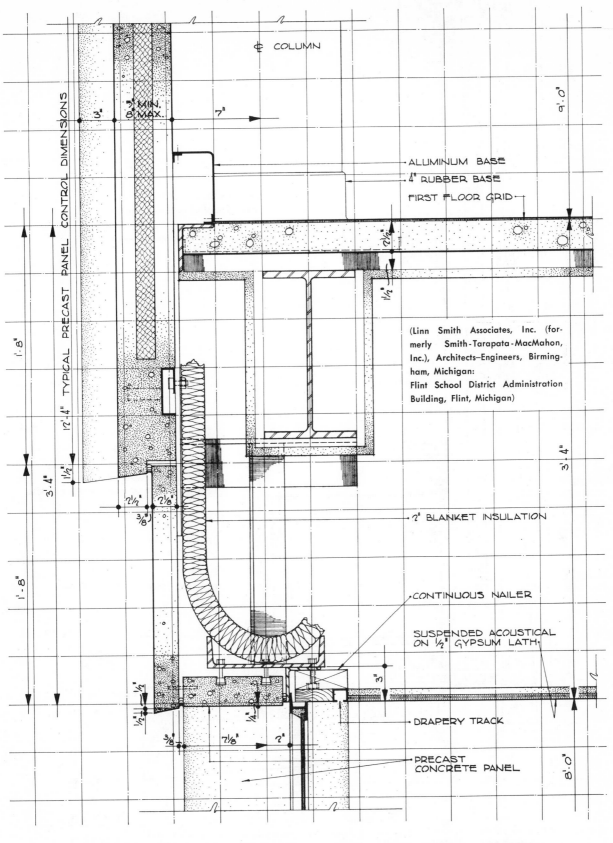

C COLUMN

ALUMINUM BASE
4" RUBBER BASE
FIRST FLOOR GRID

TYPICAL PRECAST PANEL CONTROL DIMENSIONS

5" MIN.
8" MAX.

3"

7"

9'-0"

12'-4"

1'-8"

3'-4"

1'-8"

1½"

2½"

2⅛"

3/8"

½"

¼"

3/8"

7⅛"

2"

8'-0"

3'-4"

(Linn Smith Associates, Inc. (formerly Smith-Tarapata-MacMahon, Inc.), Architects–Engineers, Birmingham, Michigan:
Flint School District Administration Building, Flint, Michigan)

2" BLANKET INSULATION

CONTINUOUS NAILER

SUSPENDED ACOUSTICAL ON ½" GYPSUM LATH.

3"

DRAPERY TRACK

PRECAST CONCRETE PANEL

FIGURE 4-13.   DETAIL - SECTION OF STEEL FRAME STRUCTURE

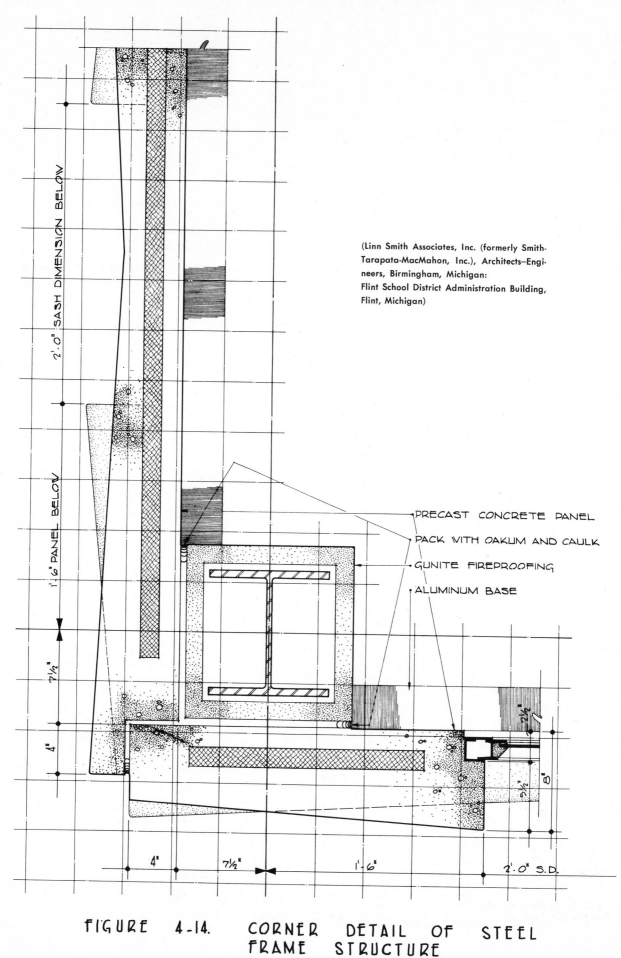

(Linn Smith Associates, Inc. (formerly Smith-Tarapata-MacMahon, Inc.), Architects–Engineers, Birmingham, Michigan:
Flint School District Administration Building, Flint, Michigan)

PRECAST CONCRETE PANEL

PACK WITH OAKUM AND CAULK

GUNITE FIREPROOFING

ALUMINUM BASE

2'-0" SASH DIMENSION BELOW

1'-6" PANEL BELOW

7½"

4"

4"

7½"

1'-6"

2'-0" S.D.

FIGURE 4-14. CORNER DETAIL OF STEEL FRAME STRUCTURE

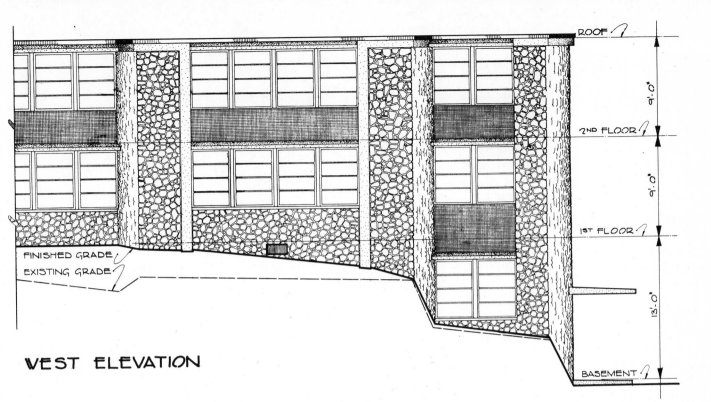

VEST ELEVATION

FINISHED GRADE

EXISTING GRADE

ROOF

2ND FLOOR

1ST FLOOR

BASEMENT

9'-0"

9'-0"

13'-0"

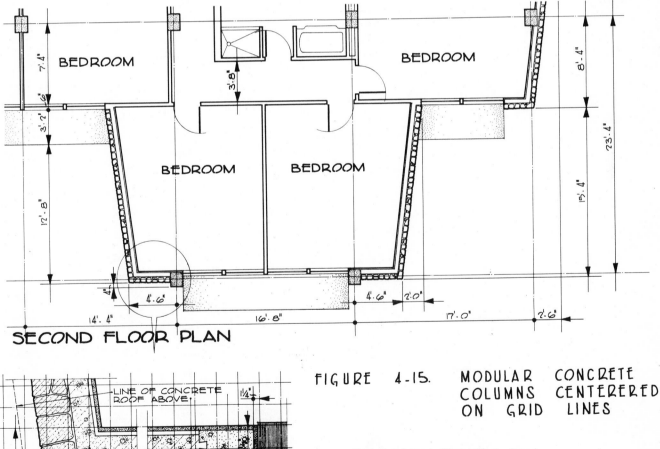

BEDROOM

BEDROOM

BEDROOM

BEDROOM

7'-4"

3'-8"

8'-4"

3'-2"

23'-4"

15'-4"

12'-8"

4"

4'-6"

4'-6"

2'-0"

14'-4"

16'-8"

17'-0"

2'-6"

SECOND FLOOR PLAN

LINE OF CONCRETE ROOF ABOVE

1¼"

12"

DETAIL

4'-6"

6"

FIGURE 4-15. MODULAR CONCRETE COLUMNS CENTERERED ON GRID LINES

(Aeck Associates, Architects, Atlanta, Georgia:
Girls' Dormitory, Tallulah Falls School, Tallulah Falls, Georgia)

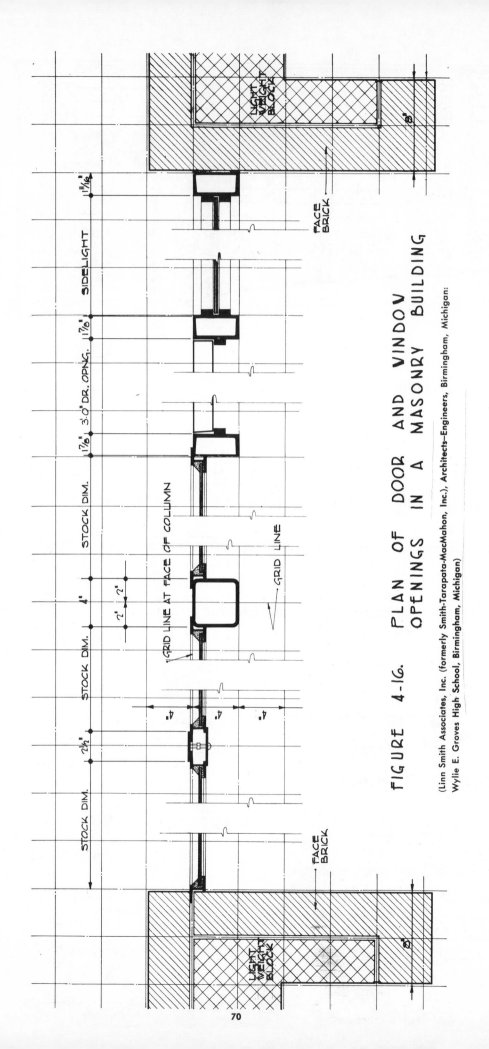

FIGURE 4-16. PLAN OF DOOR AND WINDOW OPENINGS IN A MASONRY BUILDING

(Linn Smith Associates, Inc. (formerly Smith-Tarapata-MacMahon, Inc.), Architects-Engineers, Birmingham, Michigan: Wylie E. Groves High School, Birmingham, Michigan)

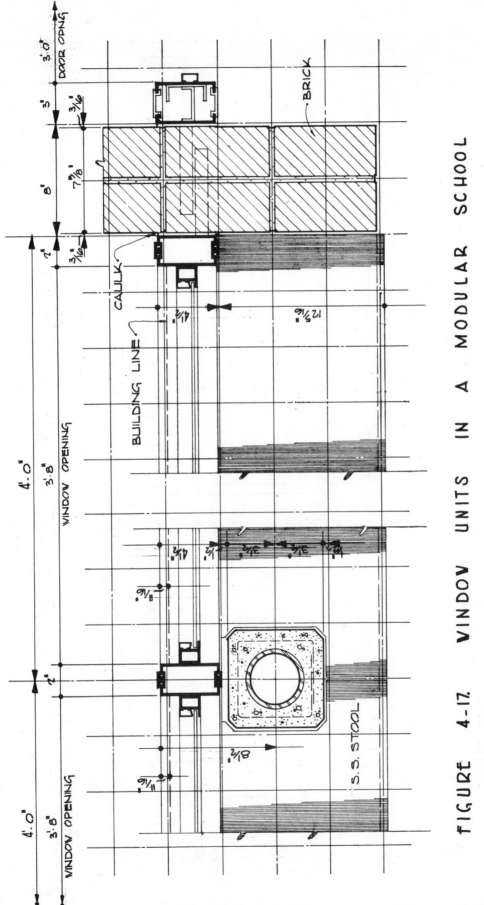

FIGURE 4-17. WINDOW UNITS IN A MODULAR SCHOOL

(Linn Smith Associates, Inc., Architects–Engineers, Birmingham, Michigan:
Addition to Pembroke School, Birmingham, Michigan)

71

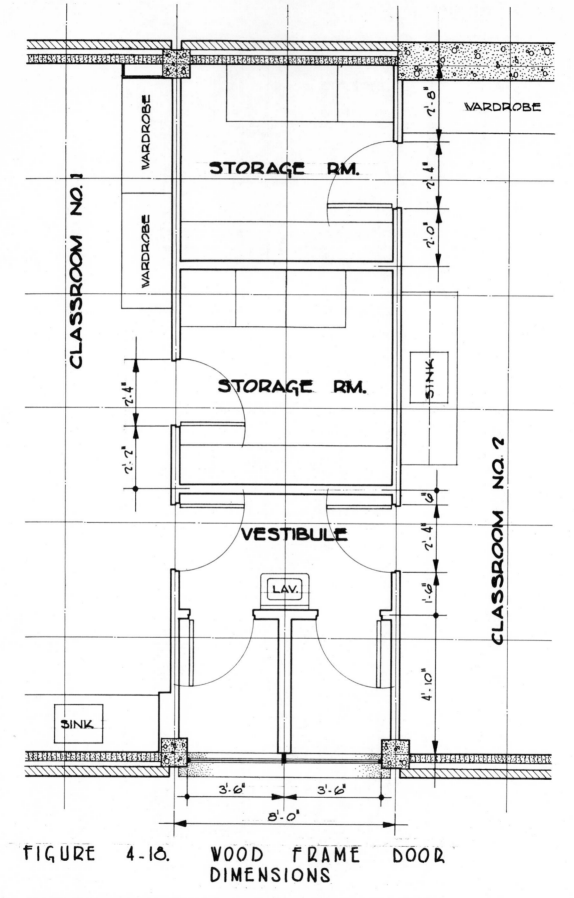

FIGURE 4-18. WOOD FRAME DOOR DIMENSIONS

(Lionel H. Abshire and Associates; Robert P. Sprague, Associate; Architects, Baton Rouge, Louisiana: South Greenville Elementary School, Baton Rouge, Louisiana)

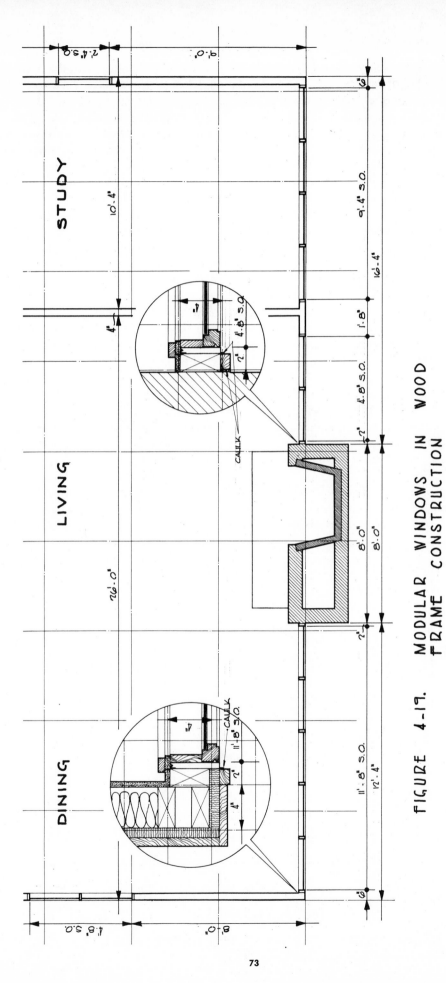

FIGURE 4-19. MODULAR WINDOWS IN WOOD
FRAME CONSTRUCTION

(Robert P. Darlington, Architect, Pullman, Washington:
Community Congregational Church Parsonage, Pullman, Washington)

curved building wall and a curved grid line is used to dimension the exterior surface.

The character of a particular job, as well as local construction practices, will determine the specific modular-dimensioning technique. Actually, the technique is not as important as remembering that modular dimensioning is a reference method for simplifying the design, working drawings, and construction of buildings, and is most successful when modular coordination of all parts of a building is an integral part of the design process.

DOORS AND WINDOWS

The simplest method of dimensioning a door or window is to show a modular dimension for the wall opening or for the column or mullion spacing into which it will fit. The door and window schedules list the correctly sized unit or units to fit the opening, and the details show the method of installation. If the door or window is not modular, there is opportunity for the architect to adjust to the modular opening by the design of the jamb or the mullion detail. Within limits, construction tolerances permit some adjustment of nonmodular units to fit modular openings.

In the case of a door component, the door and its frame come as a unit and the modular dimension is given for the whole unit. Where the doors alone

are listed by size and type in the door schedule, the plan dimension is usually given to the actual door size. Thus, modular doors are 2′0″, 2′8″, 3′0″, and other multiples of 4 inches.

Doors and windows in masonry construction. The plan of a door and window opening in a masonry high school is illustrated in Figure 4-16. The over-all opening is a modular dimension, but is filled with units none of which is modular except the 3′0″ door. The only grid lines shown are the ones at the masonry wall at each end and the one through the center of the 4-inch steel column, which serves as a reference line and check point.

The dimensioning of modular materials is handled in the same way, and results in greater simplicity of coordination and dimensioning. This is the case in Figure 4-17, in which all the window units are modular except those at the ends, which are shorter by the thickness of half a mullion. This allows a continuous 4′0″ modular reference grid to be carried through the building with a desirable sparcity of dimensions.

Doors and windows in wood frame construction. The application of modular dimensions to a door opening rather than to a rough opening is shown in Figure 4-18. In these wood-frame partitions, each door and its frame are not a single component. The architect, therefore, has preferred to dimension actual door sizes as they are listed in the door sched-

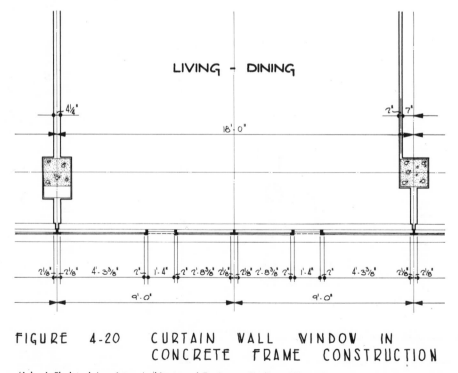

FIGURE 4-20   CURTAIN WALL WINDOW IN CONCRETE FRAME CONSTRUCTION

(John J. Flad and Associates, Architects and Engineers, Madison, Wisconsin: Wisland Corporation Apartment Building, Madison, Wisconsin)

ule. Details on another sheet of the working drawings show the design of the frame and the location of the rough framing members on each side of the door. In this plan, the modular door widths coincide with the 4-inch grid, and their dimensions are shown with arrows. If the same widths did not fall on the grid, the dimensions would be shown with dots.

The same dimensioning techniques are used with windows. The modular wood windows in the plan in Figure 4-19 do not fall on the grid and are dimensioned with dots. However, a 2-inch framing dimension at each end spaces them properly with relation to the grid and maintains an over-all modular opening for windows and framing.

Curtain wall windows in concrete frame. In Figures 4-9, 4-10, and 4-11, a concrete-frame structure was shown in which the columns were placed inside the exterior wall. The same structure is shown in Figure 4-20 with an alternate window arrangement. The windows themselves are not modular, but each structural bay is repetitive and the over-all dimension of the fixed and movable units equals the modular dimension of the structural-reference grid.

Windows in steel frame. Another example of the treatment of windows is illustrated in Figures 4-12, 4-13, and 4-14. The building shown is a steel-frame structure in which the exterior wall consists of precast concrete panels hung on the steel frame. The windows are formed by the spaces between the panels and are made of modular steel sash. There is no distinct modular relationship between the exterior panel/window wall and the structural grid of the columns or the smaller reference grid, although all are modular and are coordinated by the 4-inch modular grid.

PARTITIONS

The modular grid is usually established at the nominal exterior face of a building with a specific relationship to the foundation wall and to definite building elements such as columns. Dimensions to interior partitions are developed from the same locations, with the grid serving as the modular reference system.

Wood frame. In wood-frame construction, the logical place to locate partitions is centered between grid lines. This gives a modular dimension from

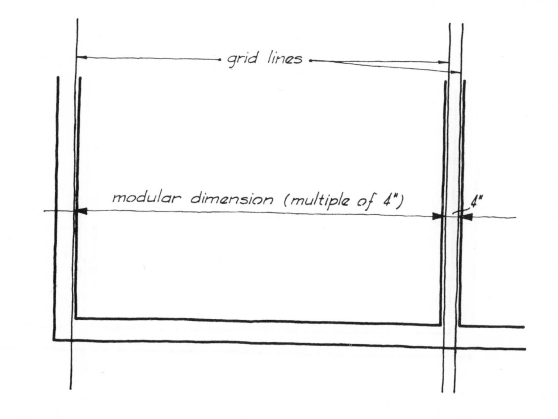

FIGURE 4-21.   STUD PARTITION CENTERED
BETWEEN GRID LINES

the nominal stud face of the interior partition to the nominal stud face of the exterior wall, which is also centered between grid lines, as in Figures 4-5 and 4-6. If the partitions are centered on a grid line, the modular room dimension is lost in the rooms along the exterior wall of a building. A comparison of the two methods is shown in Figures 4-21 and 4-22.

Brick veneer. An exception to the general rule of centering partitions between grid lines sometimes exists in the case of brick-veneer construction. In Figure 4-23, the first grid line on the brick-veneer wall is located half a joint width outside the face of the brick and the foundation wall. The second grid line is half a joint width past the inside face of the brick, and the stud wall is centered on the third grid line. In order to maintain a modular dimension between the nominal interior face of this stud wall and the nominal faces of partition studs, the partitions should also be centered on grid lines.

An alternative is to center the brick wall on the first grid line, and to center both the stud wall behind it and the interior partitions between grid lines. This would be particularly appropriate when only a relatively small portion of the structure is brick veneer and the rest is frame construction.

Modular-dimensioning technique at partitions. On small-scale plans, $\frac{3}{4}'' = 1'0''$ and smaller, all dimensions are nominal, that is, to a nominal face rather than to an actual face. No fractions are necessary unless a nominal face itself is at a fractional distance from a grid line. Dimensions to partitions, as explained in the modular note on the first sheet of the working drawings, are to nominal faces unless a specific note or detail points out a variation. The conventional modular-dimensioning system on small-scale plans is shown in Figure 4-24. Arrows indicate dimensions to nominal partition faces at grid lines, and dots show the location of nominal faces off the grid when a partition is centered on a grid line.

Partitions off grid. When a partition is neither centered between grid lines nor centered on a grid line, as in Figure 4-25, the dimensions are still given to the nominal faces and are indicated by dots.

Partitions over 4 inches. Partitions which are thicker than 4 inches cannot be centered between grid lines, and are treated by locating one nominal face on a grid line and dimensioning to it with an

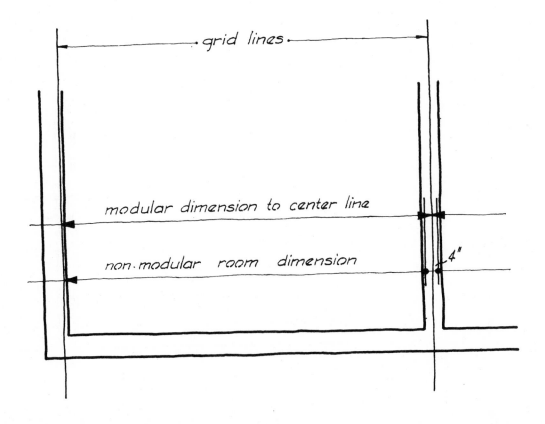

FIGURE 4-22.   STUD PARTITION CENTERED
ON GRID LINE

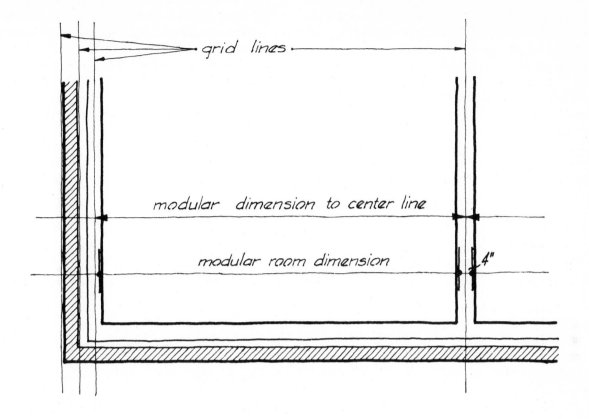

FIGURE   4·23.   STUD PARTITION IN BRICK
VENEER CONSTRUCTION

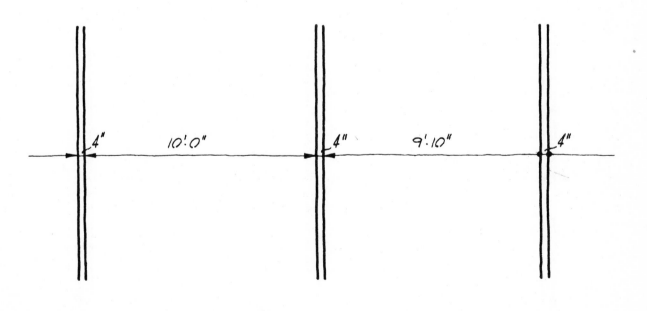

FIGURE   4·24.   CONVENTIONAL MODULAR DIMENSIONING
SYSTEM ON SMALL-SCALE PLANS

arrow. The other nominal face is shown with a dot.
If both faces are off the grid, dots locate the nominal
faces. These conditions are shown in Figure 4-26.

MODULAR NOTE FOR CONTRACTORS

A specific note for the contractor should be placed
on the first sheet of working drawings to alert him

that the drawings are modular. It also increases
the possibility of deriving bidding benefits and helps
to forestall confusion and questions during the construction period. The modular note should be clear
and simple and should usually be accompanied by
a sketch or two illustrating the dimensioning
method.

A standard note on modular dimensioning, illus-

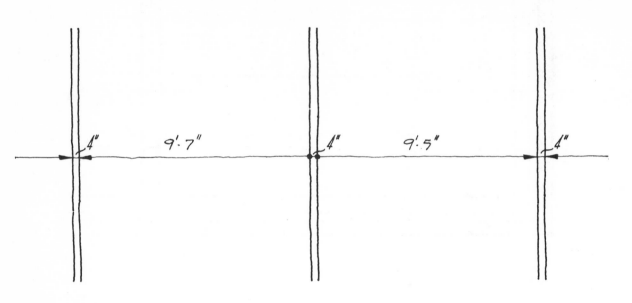

FIGURE 4-25   PARTITION NOT CENTERED BETWEEN GRID
LINES NOR ON A GRID LINE

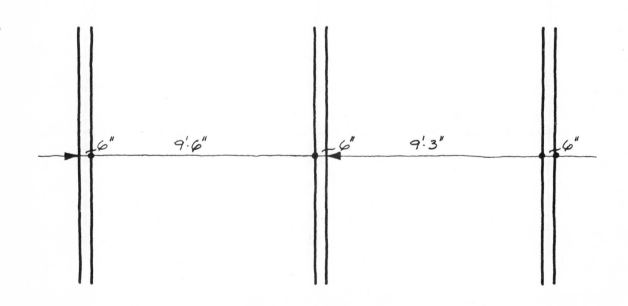

FIGURE 4-26.   PARTITIONS THICKER THAN
FOUR INCHES

NOTE—All drawings are dimensioned by The Modular Method

*in conformance with the American Standard Basis for Coordination
of Dimensions of Building Materials and Equipment, A62.1*

*This system of dimensioning is used for greater efficiency in construction: less
cutting, fitting and waste of material, less chance for dimensional errors. The
Modular Method uses a horizontal and vertical grid of reference lines. The
gridlines are spaced 4 inches apart in length, width and height.*

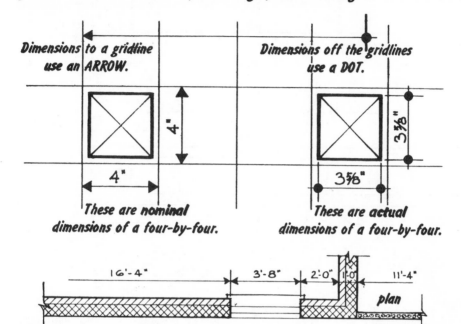

*Dimensions to a gridline
use an ARROW.*

*These are nominal
dimensions of a four-by-four.*

*Dimensions off the gridlines
use a DOT.*

*These are actual
dimensions of a four-by-four.*

*SMALL-SCALE plans, elevations and sections ordinarily give only nominal and
grid dimensions (from gridline to gridline in multiples of four inches, using
arrows at both ends). Dimension-arrows thus indicate **nominal** faces of walls,
jambs, etc., finish floor, etc., coinciding with invisible gridlines, which are not
drawn in at such small scales.*

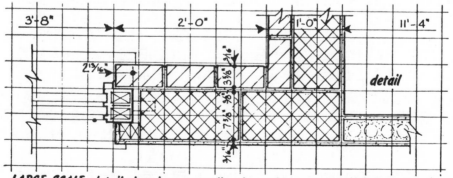

*LARGE-SCALE detail drawings actually show these same gridlines drawn in,
every 4 inches. On these details, reference dimensions give the locations of
actual faces of materials in relation to the grid.*

FIGURE 4.27.   STANDARD MODULAR NOTE

IMPORTANT !

SAVES TIME AND MATERIAL

• ESTIMATING - CHECKING - LAYOUT - PLACING

DOTS AND ARROWHEADS

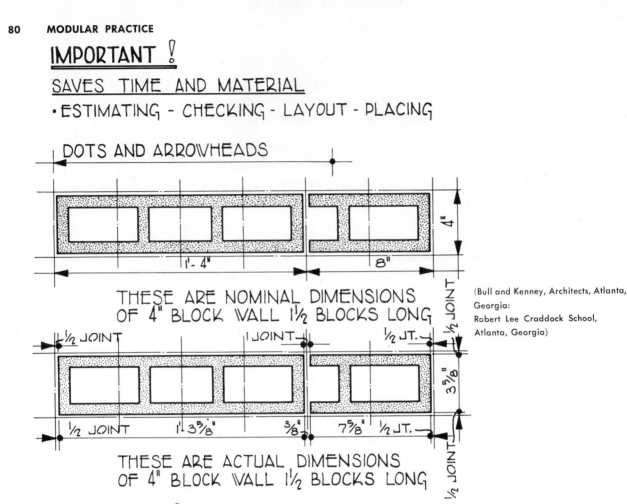

THESE ARE NOMINAL DIMENSIONS
OF 4" BLOCK WALL 1½ BLOCKS LONG

(Bull and Kenney, Architects, Atlanta, Georgia:
Robert Lee Craddock School, Atlanta, Georgia)

THESE ARE ACTUAL DIMENSIONS
OF 4" BLOCK WALL 1½ BLOCKS LONG

IMPORTANT !

SPECIAL NOTES FOR THIS JOB

• CONCRETE BLOCK - ALWAYS CENTERED BETWEEN GRID LINES;
IN LAYOUT, SNAP 2 LINES 4" APART ON THE SLAB AND LAY 4"
PARTITION BLOCK BETWEEN THEM.

• NO FRACTIONS - ACTUAL FACE IS ½ JOINT BACK FROM NOMI-
NAL FACE; ONLY EXCEPTION IS 1-STORY LOBBY WING.
SEE ①/A.3 FOR COURSING IN CLASSROOMS AND CORRIDOR - ONLY
FULL AND HALF LENGTH BLOCK REQUIRED - NO WASTE. ALL
BLOCK DIMENSIONS ON PLANS ARE NOMINAL.

• BRICK - ALWAYS CENTERED ON A GRID LINE; NOMINAL FACE 2"
FROM GRID LINE AND ACTUAL FACE ½ JOINT BACK FROM
NOMINAL FACE. ALL BRICK DIMENSIONS ON PLANS ARE NOM-
INAL.

• POREX SOFFIT MATERIAL - ALL 4 EDGES OF ALL PANELS ARE
2" FROM A GRID LINE; NOMINAL FACE IS ALSO THE ACTUAL FACE.

• CONCRETE - SEE MODULAR DIMENSIONING NOTES AND DIA-
GRAMS ON SHEET S-1

FIGURE   4-28.   SUPPLEMENTARY   MODULAR   NOTE
FOR   A   SPECIFIC   PROJECT

MODULAR DIMENSIONING NOTE TO CONTRACTOR

- THESE DRAWINGS USE <u>MODULAR DIMENSIONING</u> THROUGHOUT.
- AN IMAGINARY 4" GRID IS SUPERIMPOSED ON ALL DRAWINGS. WITH FEW EXCEPTIONS, MATERIALS ARE PLACED ON THIS GRID AND DIMENSIONS ARE GIVEN TO THE GRID. ONLY NECESSARY GRID LINES ARE SHOWN ON ANY DRAWINGS.
- NOTE THE FOLLOWING:
  1. MOST DIMENSIONS HAVE NO FRACTIONS BECAUSE THEY ARE TO THE GRID LINES.
  2. ALL 4" PARTITIONS ARE CENTERED <u>BETWEEN</u> GRID LINES EXCEPT WHERE NOTED.
  3. ALL DIMENSIONS ON SMALL SCALE PLANS, ELEVATIONS AND SECTIONS (3/4" = 1'.0" AND SMALLER) ARE CONSIDERED NOMINAL, I.E., TO THE NOMINAL FACE OF A MATERIAL, NOT THE ACTUAL FACE.

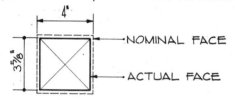

4"x 4" SHOWING NOMINAL & ACTUAL FACES

  4. LARGE SCALE DETAILS (OVER 3/4" = 1'.0") SHOW ACTUAL CONDITIONS.

- IMPORTANT: ALL DIMENSIONS TO A GRID LINE ARE SHOWN BY AN <u>ARROW-HEAD</u>. ALL DIMENSIONS NOT TO A GRID LINE ARE SHOWN BY A <u>DOT</u>.

EXAMPLES OF MODULAR DIMENSIONING

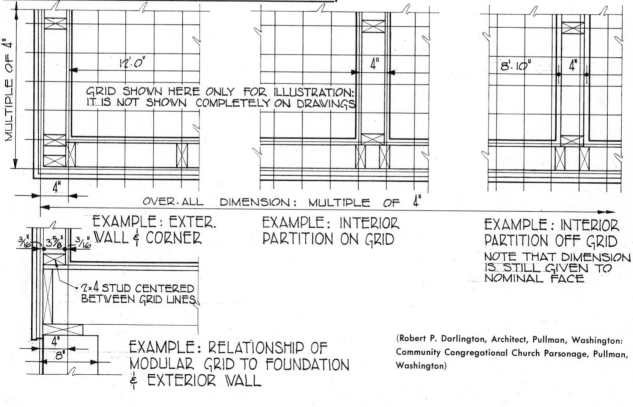

(Robert P. Darlington, Architect, Pullman, Washington: Community Congregational Church Parsonage, Pullman, Washington)

FIGURE 4-29. COMPLETE MODULAR NOTE FOR A SPECIFIC PROJECT

NOTE – ALL DRAWINGS ARE DIMENSIONED BY THE MODULAR METHOD.
THIS SYSTEM OF DIMENSIONING IS USED FOR GREATER EFFICIENCY IN
DRAFTING AND CONSTRUCTION WITH LESS CHANCE OF DIMENSIONAL
ERROR. THE MODULAR METHOD USES A HORIZONTAL AND VERTICAL
SERIES OF REFERENCE PLANES, THE GRID, SPACED 4" APART IN LENGTH,
WIDTH, AND HEIGHT. DIMENSION LINES ARE TERMINATED WITH A SLASH
MARK IF ON THE GRID AND A DOT IF OFF THE GRID. NOMINAL MATERIALS,
BRICK, BLOCK, ETC. WILL BE DIMENSIONED TO THEIR NOMINAL FACE ON OR
OFF THE GRID UNLESS OTHERWISE NOTED.

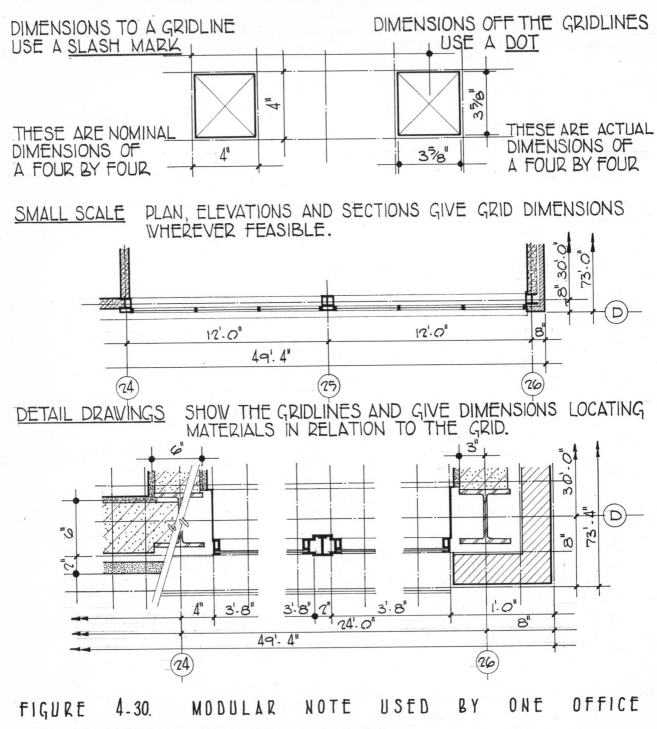

FIGURE   4-30.   MODULAR   NOTE   USED   BY   ONE   OFFICE

(Sargent, Webster, Crenshaw and Folley, Architects and Engineers, Syracuse, New York)

THESE ARE STANDARD MODULAR WORKING DRAWINGS

IN CONFORMANCE WITH THE CODE FOR MODULAR CO-ORDINATION IN BUILDING. CSA·A·31·1959

THE POSITION, AND USUALLY THE SIZE OF BUILDING COMPONENTS IN THESE DRAWINGS ARE CONTROLLED BY THE STANDARD MODULAR GRID OF 4 INCHES. THE LARGE SCALE DRAWINGS SHOW IN CLEAR DETAIL THE FITTING OF COMPONENTS TO THE GRID.

DIMENSION LINES TAKEN TO THE GRID ALWAYS HAVE AN ARROWHEAD ────▶

DIMENSION LINES TAKEN TO POINTS NOT ON THE GRID ALWAYS HAVE A DOT ───●

THE DIMENSIONS OF THE MANUFACTURED COMPONENTS SHOWN IN THE LARGE SCALE DETAIL AS 3⅝" AND 7⅝" ARE THE MANUFACTURER DIMENSIONS.

THE MODULAR DIMENSIONS OF THESE COMPONENTS ARE CONSIDERED AS 4" AND 8"

THE 3⁄16" DIMENSION IS THE CONSTANT RELATIONSHIP OF THESE PARTICULAR COMPONENTS TO THE CONTROLLING GRID.

THE SMALL SCALE PLAN AND ELEVATION SHOW ASSEMBLY OF COMPONENTS. MOST OF THE DIMENSIONS GIVEN ARE MODULAR DIMENSIONS RUNNING TO THE CONTROLLING GRID LINES AND ARE IN MULTIPLES OF 4 INCHES. BY APPLYING THE ARROWHEAD CONVENTION IT IS CLEAR WHICH DIMENSIONS ARE TO THE GRID LINE.

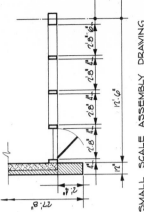

SMALL SCALE ASSEMBLY DRAWING

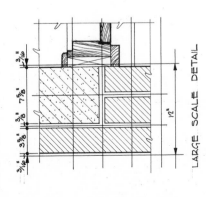

LARGE SCALE DETAIL

FIGURE 4.31. CANADIAN MODULAR NOTE

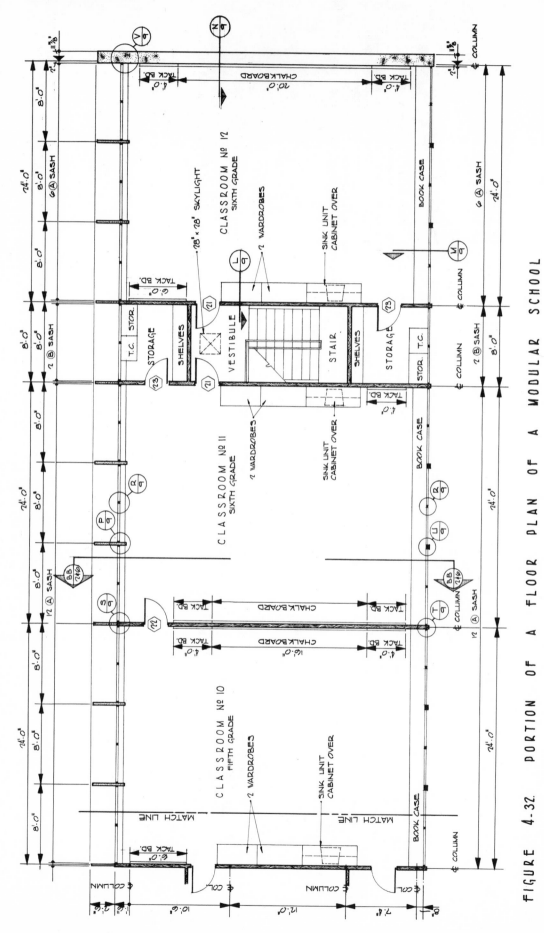

FIGURE 4-32.   PORTION OF A FLOOR PLAN OF A MODULAR SCHOOL

(Lionel H. Abshire and Associates; Robert P. Sprague, Associate; Architects, Baton Rouge, Louisiana:
South Greenville Elementary School, Baton Rouge, Louisiana)

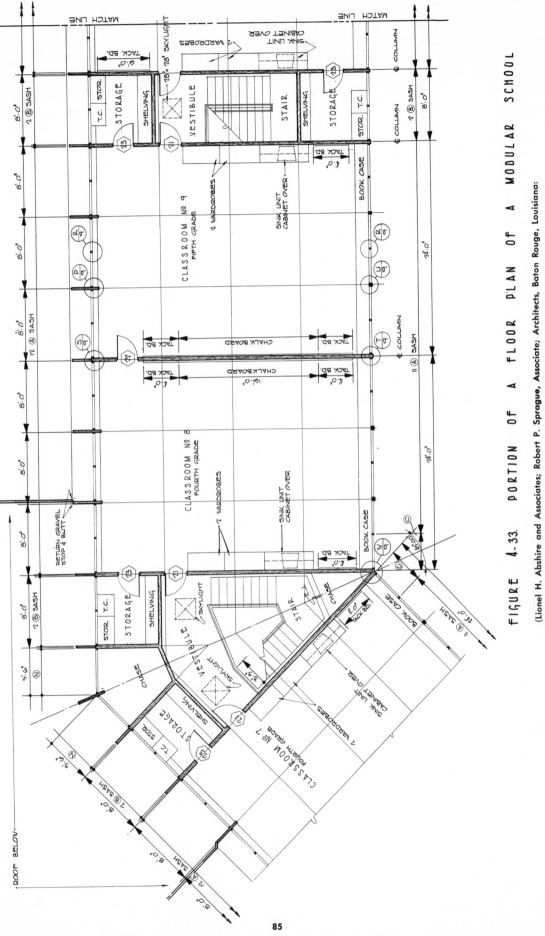

FIGURE 4-33.   PORTION OF A FLOOR PLAN OF A MODULAR SCHOOL

(Lionel H. Abshire and Associates; Robert P. Sprague, Associate; Architects, Baton Rouge, Louisiana:
South Greenville Elementary School, Baton Rouge, Louisiana)

trated in Figure 4-27, has been available for a number of years for application directly to the original working drawings. This note was developed by the AIA Modular Coordinator and was recommended by the Modular Measure Committee of the American Standards Association.

Many architects want a more specific note or a more complete statement and prefer to supplement the standard note with additional information or to develop their own modular note. The standard note states that grid lines are always shown on large-scale details; however, because many offices find it desirable not to show grid lines on details, or on any drawings, a change in notation and explanation is necessary.

Supplementary information about modular dimensioning may vary from one project to another and will contain specific references to one project only. A supplemental note used by one office for a specific project is shown in Figure 4-28. This note appears on the drawings adjacent to the standard note.

In the example illustrated in Figure 4-29, the standard note was not used, and a complete "Modular Dimensioning Note to Contractor" was substituted. This note and the illustrative drawings accompanying it apply to the type of construction employed in the project. Changes would be required for a building having a different type of construction.

Other architects use their own variation of modular dimensioning and have their own note of explanation. An example is shown in Figure 4-30, where a slash mark replaces the arrow as the grid-line dimensioning symbol.

A proposed standard modular note for use in Canada is reproduced in Figure 4-31. It is the same in principle as the notes in the preceding figures.

A final working-drawing example is shown in Figures 4-32 and 4-33. Modular-dimensioning principles are followed and are expressed clearly in the relationship of the structural and reference grids to the implied 4-inch modular grid.

West Virginia University Hospital
Morgantown, West Virginia

C. E. Silling and Associates
Architects
Charleston, West Virginia

FUNCTION OF ELEVATIONS

Building elevations in working drawings provide information about the exterior design of a building and reveal the relationship between the exterior and important interior conditions. Materials, doors and windows, floor-to-floor dimensions, and important elevations above the base datum point are shown. Vertical section lines locate the wall sections which are shown on subsequent sheets of the working drawings, and reference marks on window and door sills, jambs and heads, and other specific areas refer to large-scale details. Elevations are customarily drawn at the same scale as the floor plans.

FUNCTION OF SECTIONS

Wall sections are cross-sectional drawings usually taken vertically through exterior walls and showing the specific relationships between parts of the building, material-to-material relationships, floor, ceiling, sill, and head heights, and the location of pipes, ducts, and other items of mechanical and electrical equipment. In addition to exterior-wall sections, sections are taken through other pertinent portions of the building for the purpose of explaining the construction.

GRIDS, ELEVATIONS, AND SECTIONS

Reference and structural grids. The reference and structural grid lines which are drawn on the floor plans are used to coordinate the elevations with the plans. They are repeated vertically on the elevations or, to avoid the confusion caused by extra lines, are drawn above or below the elevations.

A portion of the elevation of the school-district administration building shown in part-plan in Figure 4-12 is illustrated in Figure 5-1. The 5'0" reference grid of the floor plan is superimposed on the elevation for reference in identifying specific portions of the elevation and in relating the elevation and the floor plans. Each fifth reference grid line, at 25'0" centers, is also a structural grid line through the center of a column. The columns are not expressed on the exterior of this building, but their location on the drawings can be determined by the dotted indication of their supporting piers and footings.

A small-scale building section and a large-scale wall section for this same project are shown in Figures 5-2 and 4-13. The use of the modular grid for reference and for the coordination of materials is seen in both of these drawings. In Figure 4-13, the architect chose to show the complete 4-inch modular grid as an aid in visualizing the coordination of the parts.

5

ELEVATIONS AND SECTIONS

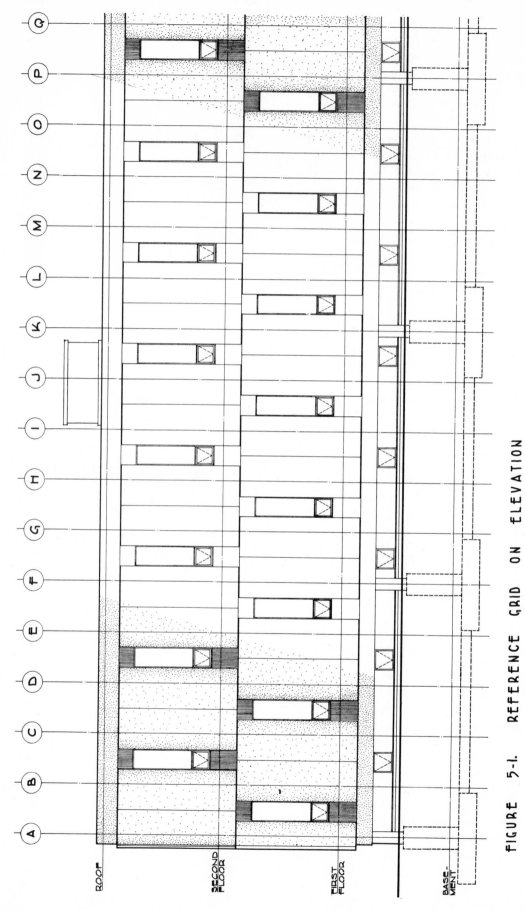

FIGURE 5-1.   REFERENCE GRID ON ELEVATION

(Linn Smith Associates, Inc. (formerly Smith-Tarapata-MacMahon, Inc.), Architects–Engineers, Birmingham, Michigan: Flint School District Administration Building, Flint, Michigan)

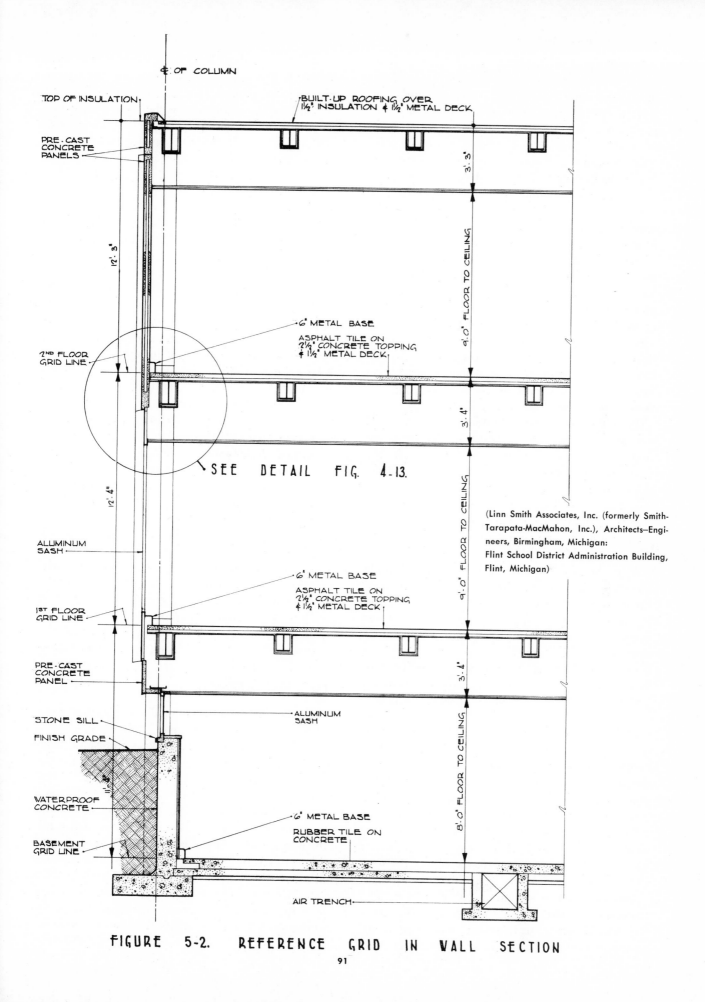

Labels on drawing:

¢ OF COLUMN

TOP OF INSULATION

BUILT-UP ROOFING OVER 1½" INSULATION & 1½" METAL DECK

PRE-CAST CONCRETE PANELS

3'-3"

12'-3"

9'-0" FLOOR TO CEILING

6" METAL BASE

ASPHALT TILE ON 2½" CONCRETE TOPPING & 1½" METAL DECK

2ND FLOOR GRID LINE

SEE DETAIL FIG. 4-13.

3'-4"

(Linn Smith Associates, Inc. (formerly Smith-Tarapata-MacMahon, Inc.), Architects–Engineers, Birmingham, Michigan: Flint School District Administration Building, Flint, Michigan)

12'-4"

9'-0" FLOOR TO CEILING

ALUMINUM SASH

6" METAL BASE

ASPHALT TILE ON 2½" CONCRETE TOPPING & 1½" METAL DECK

1ST FLOOR GRID LINE

PRE-CAST CONCRETE PANEL

3'-4"

STONE SILL

ALUMINUM SASH

FINISH GRADE

8'-0" FLOOR TO CEILING

WATERPROOF CONCRETE

6" METAL BASE

RUBBER TILE ON CONCRETE

BASEMENT GRID LINE

AIR TRENCH

FIGURE 5-2. REFERENCE GRID IN WALL SECTION

Modular grid in elevations. Modular dimensioning is used in elevations primarily to show vertical dimensions and, through the use of structural and reference grids, to coordinate the elevations with plans, sections, and details. Horizontal grid lines are seldom drawn across elevations, but the implied 4-inch modular grid is most important in determining vertical heights. Through the conventional dot and arrow dimensioning system, the modular grid is used to show the coordination of floor lines, roof lines, window sills and heads, and other important locations. Because the arrows identify the presence of grid lines at critical points, it is not necessary to show the grid or to label the extension lines which locate grid lines. Thus dimensions are kept to a minimum on elevations, and the modular character of the building is expressed simply by the use of arrows to the grid locations. It is useful in elevation drawings to give a specific starting point for construction by showing a vertical dimension from an important grid line, such as the first floor line, to a known datum point on the site.

The use of structural and reference grids, and the indication of portions of the modular grid, are shown in several other elevations. In Figure 5-3, only a structural grid is shown on the elevation because no smaller reference grid was used on the floor plan. In Figure 5-6, however, though a 4′0″ reference grid is used on the plan, only every eighth reference grid line is shown on the elevation as a structural grid.

As in the elevations in Figures 5-3 and 5-6, only the structural grid is utilized in the elevations in Figures 5-9 and 5-10. The use of the modular grid to show vertical dimensions is more obvious in Figure 5-9 because the structure is a tall, multi-story building with a definite repetition of modular floor-to-floor heights. In Figure 5-10, the floor-to-floor dimension is not modular, only nominal, and is indicated with the dot at the second floor line.

The elevation in Figure 5-12 has neither a structural nor a reference grid, but is similar to the elevation in Figure 5-9, with the modular floor-to-floor heights indicated by arrows. This elevation is drawn at $\frac{1}{16}″ = 1′0″$ to match the scale of the floor plan. The architect was able, using the small scale in plan, to draw the complete plan of each floor of a large and complex hospital on one sheet. In this small-scale elevation, all necessary information is given for comprehension of this portion of the project.

Modular grid in sections. The coordination of materials in a structure is expressed by the use of the modular grid. In most wall sections it is unnecessary to show the grid in its entirety. Its presence is indicated by arrow dimensions to key locations. Points in the section which are not on the grid can be related to it by the arrow and dot method. Off-grid dimensions should be shown only when absolutely necessary; otherwise, overdimensioning with a multitude of small dimensions will occur and the value of modular coordination and modular dimensioning will be lost. For example, in masonry buildings, the coursing of brick, block, or tile is usually the only grid indication which is needed. The use of the modular grid in sections is shown in Figures 5-4, 5-5, 5-8, 5-11, and 5-15 for several different construction types.

Specific coordinate lines of the structural and reference grids are helpful in wall-section drawings in locating portions of a section with respect to column center lines or other specific structural elements. All three grids—structural, reference, and modular—provide a physical means of comparing sections and elevations, as many of the same points in a building are shown in both types of drawings and are located with reference to the grids. This type of coordination is seen by relating the elevation in Figure 5-10 with the section in Figure 5-11.

Large-scale elevations. Portions of elevations in which the precise pattern of materials or the details of a particular feature are required are drawn using a larger scale than customarily is used for the elevation of the complete building. By means of the vertical reference grid lines, these drawings are related to the smaller-scale drawings of which they are a part. Horizontal modular grid lines are used to relate vertical dimensions on the detail to the same points on the elevation drawing. In this way, modular coordination and modular dimensioning help the architect in maintaining control over the design of the building and its graphic presentation.

TYPES OF SECTIONS

Small-scale sections. A small-scale section is one which is usually taken through a whole building to provide a clear picture of its basic form and structure. The size of the building will influence the scale of the section, but most often it is $\frac{3}{8}″ = 1′0″$ or smaller. Sections cannot show construction details at such small scales, but they do indicate structural relationships and the location of structural, reference, and modular grid lines. The same grid lines are easily located in large-scale sections and details, simplifying the coordination of the drawings.

Small-scale sections of several of the buildings used for plan and elevation illustrations are shown in Figures 5-2, 5-4, 5-7, and 5-14. Use of the modular grid in coordinating these drawings with the

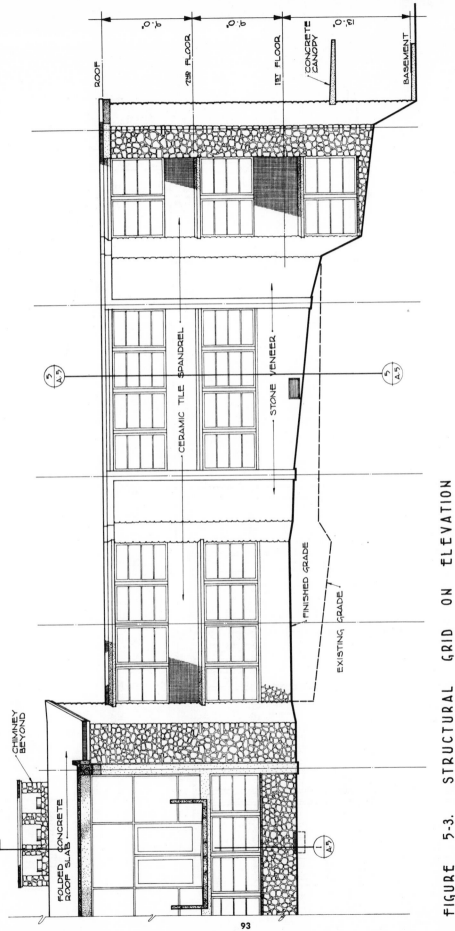

FIGURE 5-3. STRUCTURAL GRID ON ELEVATION

(Aeck Associates, Architects, Atlanta, Georgia:
Girls' Dormitory, Tallulah Falls School, Tallulah Falls, Georgia)

93

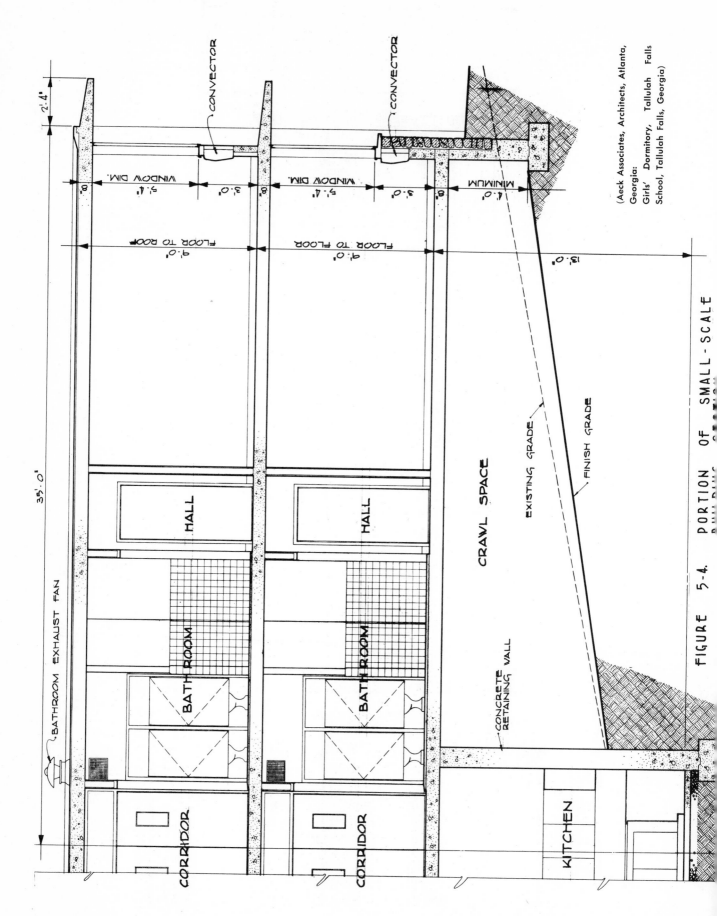

FIGURE 5-4. PORTION OF SMALL-SCALE BUILDING SECTION

(Aeck Associates, Architects, Atlanta, Georgia; Girls' Dormitory, Tallulah Falls School, Tallulah Falls, Georgia)

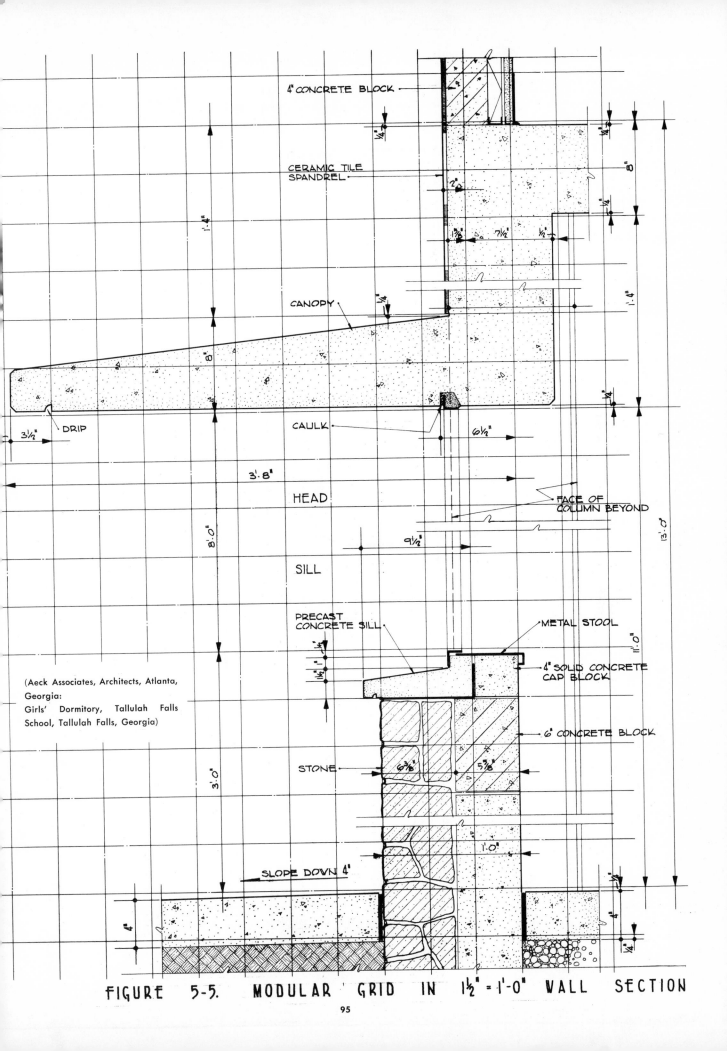

4" CONCRETE BLOCK

CERAMIC TILE
SPANDREL.

CANOPY.

DRIP

3½"

CAULK.

6½"

3'.8"

HEAD

8'.0"

SILL

9½"

FACE OF
COLUMN BEYOND

PRECAST
CONCRETE SILL.

METAL STOOL

4" SOLID CONCRETE
CAP BLOCK

6" CONCRETE BLOCK

(Aeck Associates, Architects, Atlanta,
Georgia:
Girls' Dormitory, Tallulah Falls
School, Tallulah Falls, Georgia)

STONE.

3'.0"

1'.0"

SLOPE DOWN 4"

4"

FIGURE 5-5. MODULAR GRID IN 1½" = 1'-0" WALL SECTION

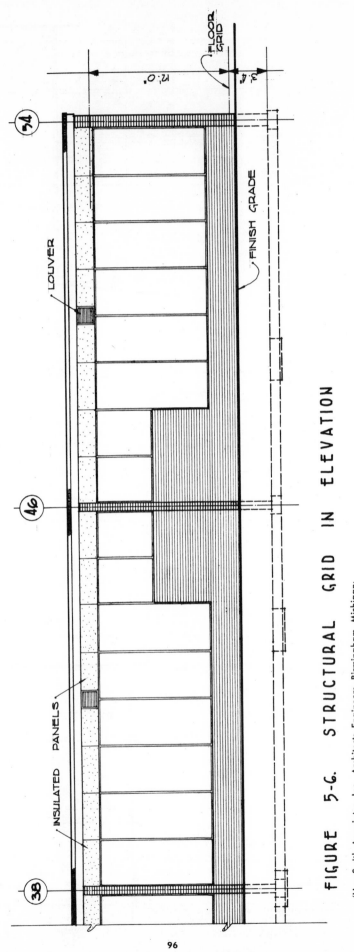

FIGURE 5-6. STRUCTURAL GRID IN ELEVATION

(Linn Smith Associates, Inc., Architects–Engineers, Birmingham, Michigan:
Addition to Pembroke School. Birmingham, Michigan)

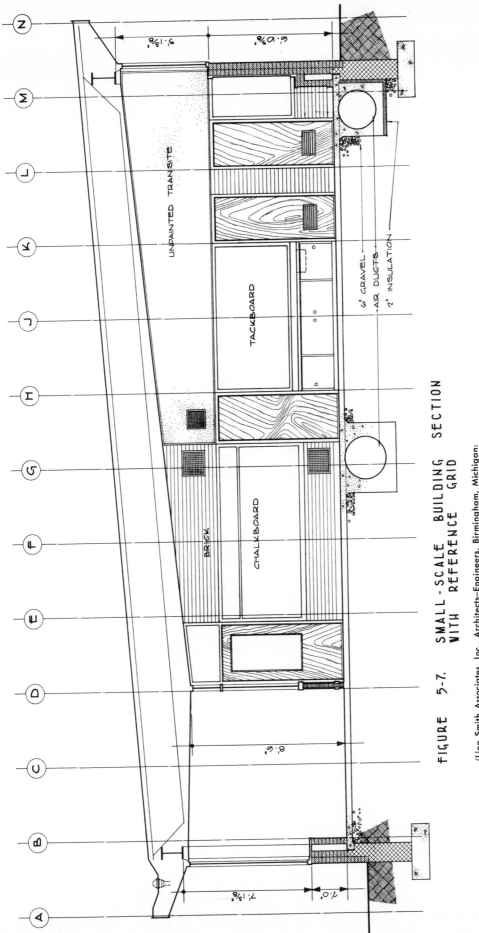

FIGURE 5-7. SMALL-SCALE BUILDING SECTION WITH REFERENCE GRID

(Linn Smith Associates, Inc., Architects–Engineers, Birmingham, Michigan: Addition to Pembroke School, Birmingham, Michigan)

97

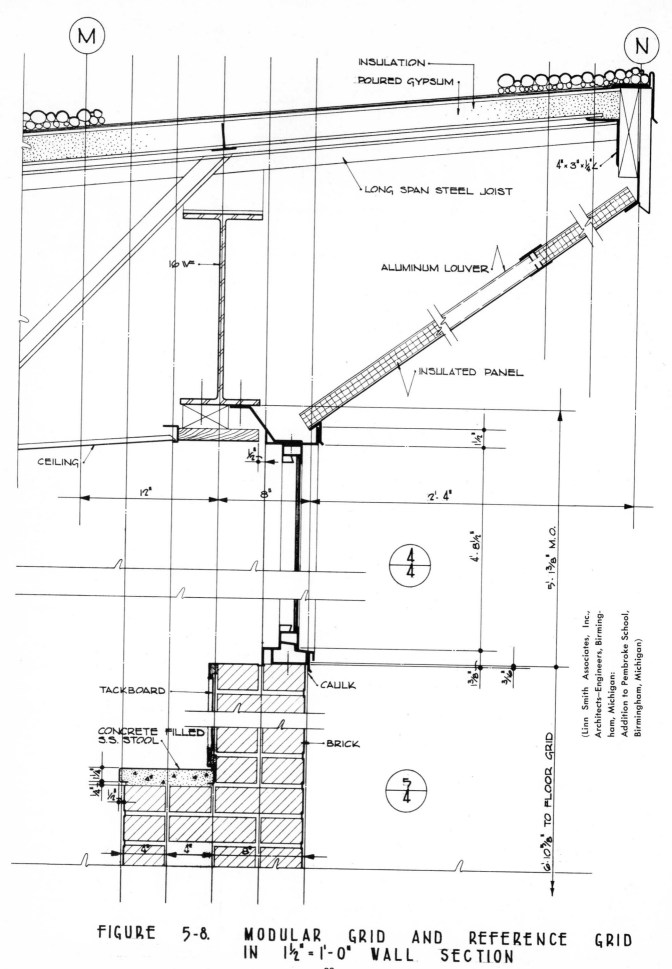

M

N

INSULATION

POURED GYPSUM

LONG SPAN STEEL JOIST

4"×3"×1¼" ∠

16 W

ALUMINUM LOUVER

INSULATED PANEL

CEILING

½"

1½"

12"

8"

2'-4"

4'-8½"

5'-1⅜" M.O.

4/4

TACKBOARD

CAULK

CONCRETE FILLED S.S. STOOL

1⅜"

3/16"

BRICK

⅛" 1½"

1½"

5/4

4"

4"

8"

6'-10⅝" TO FLOOR GRID

(Linn Smith Associates, Inc., Architects–Engineers, Birmingham, Michigan: Addition to Pembroke School, Birmingham, Michigan)

FIGURE 5-8. MODULAR GRID AND REFERENCE GRID
IN 1½"=1'-0" WALL SECTION

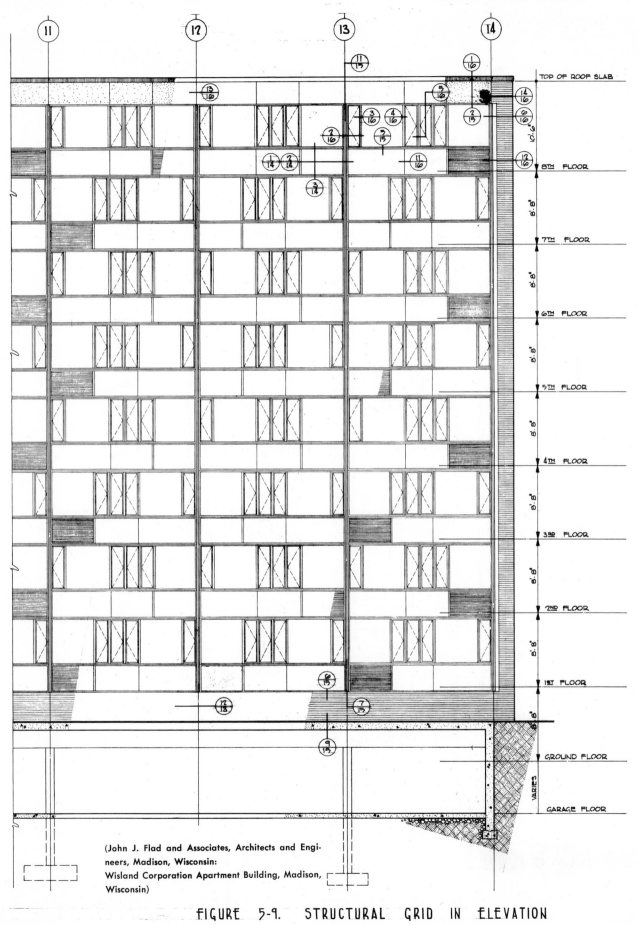

(John J. Flad and Associates, Architects and Engineers, Madison, Wisconsin:
Wisland Corporation Apartment Building, Madison, Wisconsin)

FIGURE 5-9. STRUCTURAL GRID IN ELEVATION

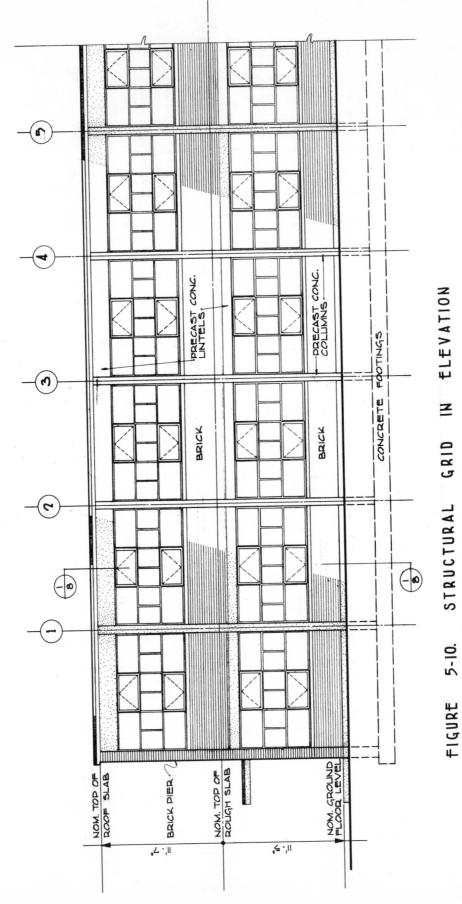

FIGURE 5-10. STRUCTURAL GRID IN ELEVATION

(Vine and Robinson, Architects, Toronto and Brampton, Ontario, Canada: Regency Acres Public School, Aurora, Ontario, Canada)

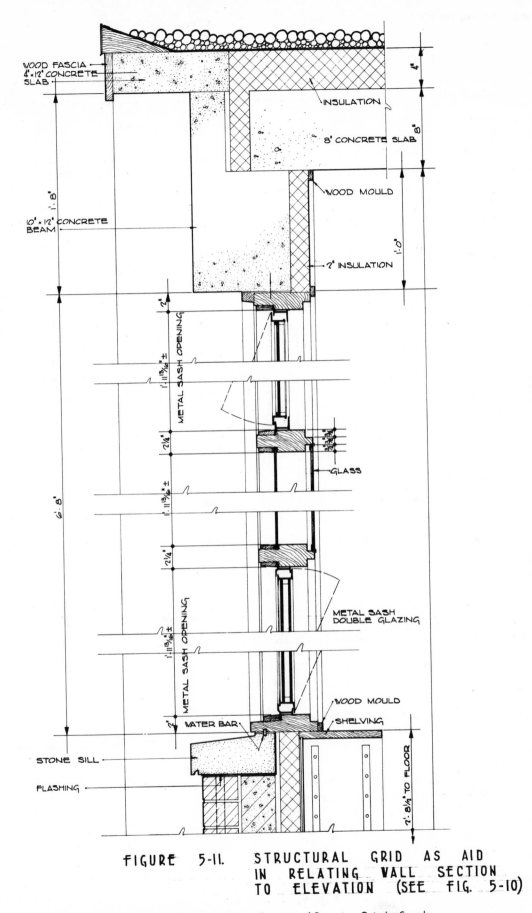

FIGURE 5-11. STRUCTURAL GRID AS AID IN RELATING WALL SECTION TO ELEVATION (SEE FIG. 5-10)

(Vine and Robinson, Architects, Toronto and Brampton, Ontario, Canada:
Regency Acres Public School, Aurora, Ontario, Canada)

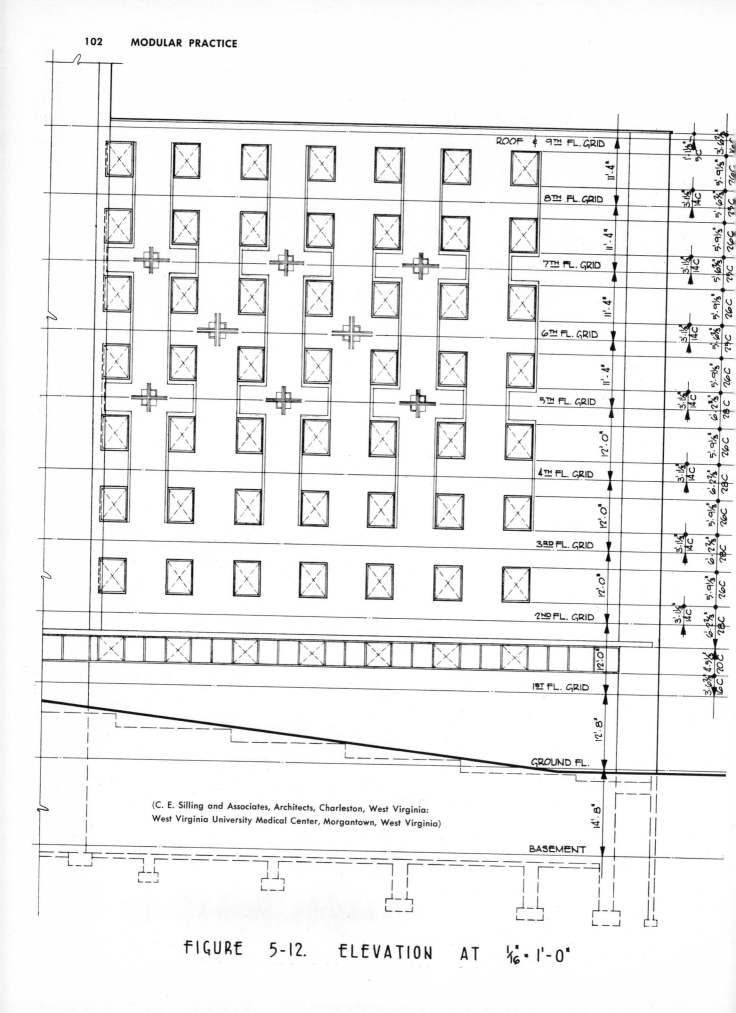

FIGURE   5-12.   ELEVATION   AT   1/16" = 1'-0"

(C. E. Silling and Associates, Architects, Charleston, West Virginia:
West Virginia University Medical Center, Morgantown, West Virginia)

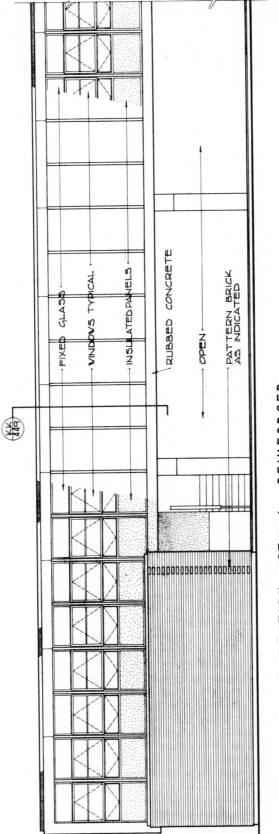

FIXED GLASS

WINDOWS TYPICAL

INSULATED PANELS

RUBBED CONCRETE

OPEN

PATTERN BRICK AS INDICATED

FIGURE 5-13.   ELEVATION OF A REINFORCED CONCRETE MODULAR SCHOOL

(Lionel H. Abshire and Associates; Robert P. Sprague, Associate; Architects, Baton Rouge, Louisiana: South Greenville Elementary School, Baton Rouge, Louisiana)

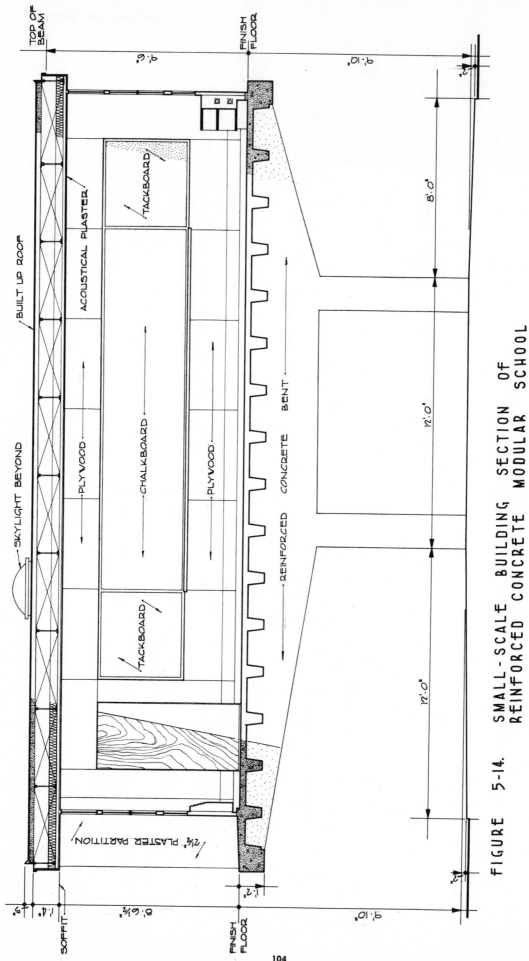

FIGURE 5-14. SMALL-SCALE BUILDING SECTION OF REINFORCED CONCRETE MODULAR SCHOOL

(Lionel H. Abshire and Associates; Robert P. Sprague, Associate; Architects, Baton Rouge, Louisiana: South Greenville Elementary School, Baton Rouge, Louisiana)

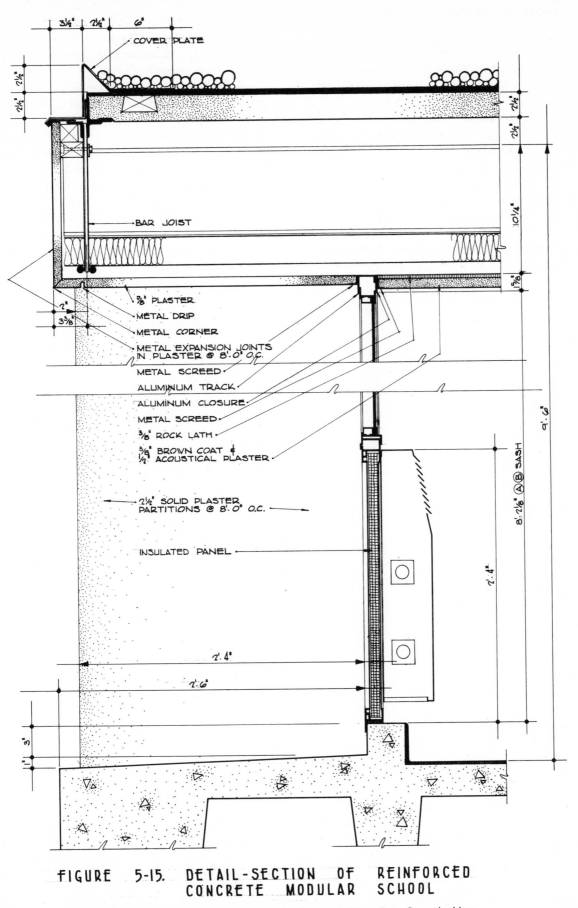

COVER PLATE

BAR JOIST

3/8" PLASTER
METAL DRIP
METAL CORNER
METAL EXPANSION JOINTS
IN PLASTER @ 8'.0" O.C.
METAL SCREED
ALUMINUM TRACK
ALUMINUM CLOSURE
METAL SCREED
3/8" ROCK LATH
3/8" BROWN COAT &
1/2" ACOUSTICAL PLASTER

2 1/2" SOLID PLASTER
PARTITIONS @ 8'.0" O.C.

INSULATED PANEL

2'.4"

2'.6"

8'-2 1/2 (A) (B) SASH

2'.4"

9'.6"

FIGURE 5-15. DETAIL-SECTION OF REINFORCED
CONCRETE MODULAR SCHOOL

(Lionel H. Abshire and Associates; Robert P. Sprague, Associate; Architects, Baton Rouge, Louisiana:
South Greenville Elementary School, Baton Rouge, Louisiana)

plans, elevations, and large-scale sections of the same building may be seen by comparing several drawings of one building, such as the elevation, ¼-inch section, and 1½-inch section of the girls' dormitory in Figures 5-3, 5-4, and 5-5.

Large-scale sections. Large-scale sections are drawn to give a specific picture of a small portion of a building. A scale of ½″ = 1′0″ or larger should be utilized to show the details of construction. The two most commonly used scales for these sections are ¾″ = 1′0″ and 1½″ = 1′0″. The larger of these is often employed to combine the functions of wall sections and details.

Several large-scale sections are shown in Figures 5-5, 5-8, and 5-11. In Figure 5-5 the complete 4-inch grid is shown. In Figure 5-8 only a few pertinent lines of the modular grid are drawn, and in Figure 5-11 only arrows are used to indicate the presence of the grid. In all these examples, important grid locations can be correlated with the same locations on plans, elevations, and small-scale sections for a clear understanding of the relationship of the large-scale section to the rest of the building.

The feasibility of applying modular design, coordination, and dimensioning to a building of unusual concept and structure is shown in the last three figures, 5-13, 5-14, and 5-15. The building illustrated is a two-story school of reinforced-concrete construction, designed, drawn, and built completely on modular principles.

South Greenville Elementary School
Baton Rouge, Louisiana

Lionel H. Abshire and Associates
Robert P. Sprague, Associate
Architects
Baton Rouge, Louisiana

FUNCTION OF DETAILS

Detail drawings are the key to the specific construction of a building. They are large-scale drawings of specific parts of a building which show the precise relationships of materials, methods of fastening and joining, shapes and contours, actual sizes, and points to which dimensions are taken. For accurate bidding, the coordination of materials in a building must be shown clearly.

PRESENTATION OF DETAILS

Scale. The scale of details varies from $1\frac{1}{2}'' = 1'0''$ to full size. The dividing point between the scale of wall sections and the scale of details is $1\frac{1}{2}'' = 1'0''$, and a drawing can fulfill both the functions of wall sections and details when it is presented at this scale. Traditionally, the scale of $3'' = 1'0''$, which is one-fourth full size, has been used more than any other. In modular drawings, with their simple dimensions and use of the modular grid to express the coordination of parts, many architects prefer the scale of $1\frac{1}{2}'' = 1'0''$ for the majority of their details.

Cross referencing. Cross referencing between plans, elevations, sections, and details is necessary for efficient use of the drawings by the architect, contractor, and subcontractors. Reference marks for details are shown on plans, elevations, and sections. Clear cross referencing between elevations and details enables the workmen on a building to understand the relationships involved and to proceed quickly and accurately with the work. The elevations illustrated in Chapter 5 contain a number of these reference marks which refer to the details in this chapter. A specific example of reference marks on an elevation is shown in Figure 6-1.

DETAILS AND THE MODULAR GRID

Key grid lines. The most desirable detail is one in which dimensions and grid lines are at a minimum. For dimensioning purposes, key modular grid lines are shown in the details to correspond with grid lines which occur also in sections or in other drawings. This facilitates coordination of all the drawings and eliminates confusion on the exact location of a detail. Here again the modular grid is used as a strong organizing force in the development of the drawings and in the construction of the building.

The floor plan which accompanies the elevation and details in Figure 6-1 is shown in Figure 6-2. Use of the modular grid to aid in relating the drawings to each other is shown by the arrow indications

6
DETAILS

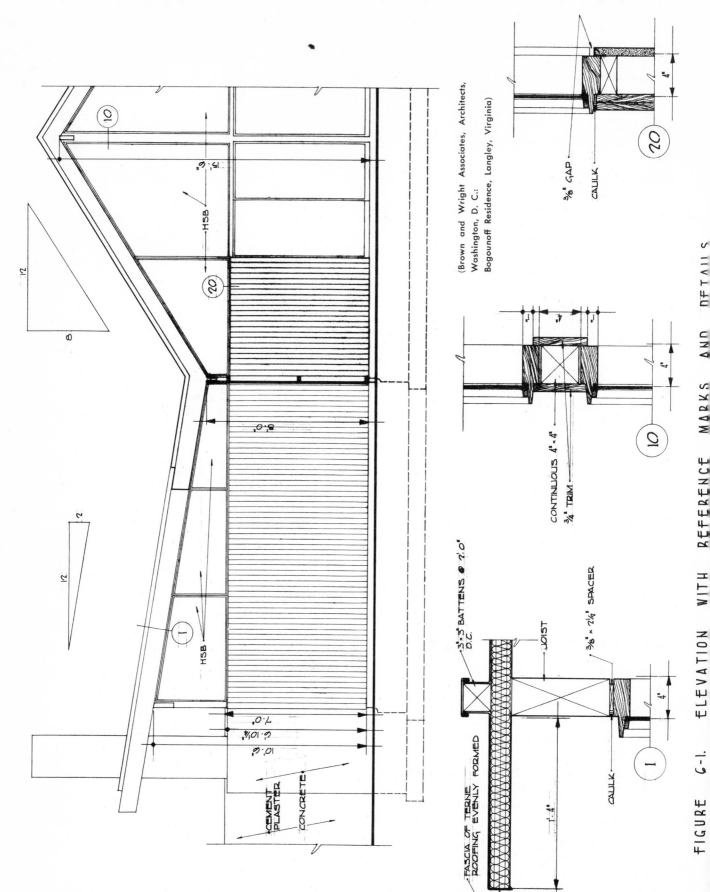

FIGURE 6-1. ELEVATION WITH REFERENCE MARKS AND DETAILS

(Brown and Wright Associates, Architects, Washington, D. C.: Bogounoff Residence, Langley, Virginia)

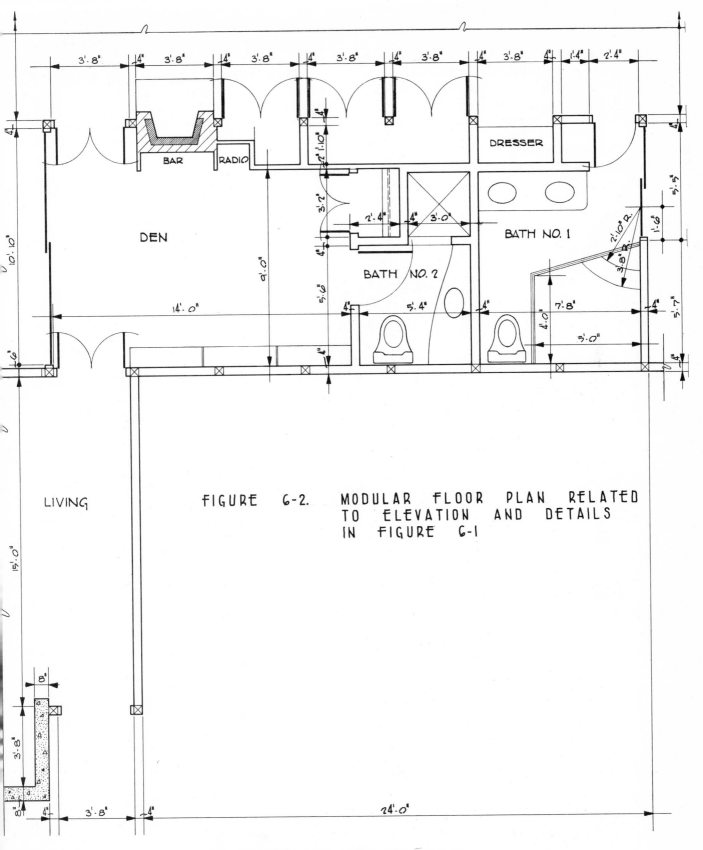

FIGURE 6-2.   MODULAR FLOOR PLAN RELATED
TO ELEVATION AND DETAILS
IN FIGURE 6-1

(Brown and Wright Associates, Architects, Washington, D. C.:
Bogounoff Residence, Langley, Virginia)

of the nominal faces of the 4-inch mullion in both Detail 10, Figure 6-1, and the floor plan in Figure 6-2.

Dimensioning.   Good details are clear and easy to read and are not cluttered with unnecessary lines, dimensions, and notes.   When key grid lines are shown in a detail, only the most pertinent dimensions are required to locate the parts of the detail with reference to the grid and to adjacent materials, as in Figures 6-1 and 6-2.   Locating a definite point or plane with respect to the modular grid results in the same minimum use of dimensions and notes for positioning materials.   This is illustrated in Figure

6-3, in which the face of the block wall is important as a reference plane for the placing of other materials, and in Figure 6-4, in which the floor line is an important reference plane.

Off-grid locations.   A dimension to the off-grid location of a major element in a detail is used when the element is too far from a grid line for its location to be determined by observation, or when it is not obviously related to another part of the detail. A simple arrow-dot dimension locates the member in question with respect to the modular grid.   The details in Figures 6-3, 6-4, and 6-5 are dimensioned in this way.

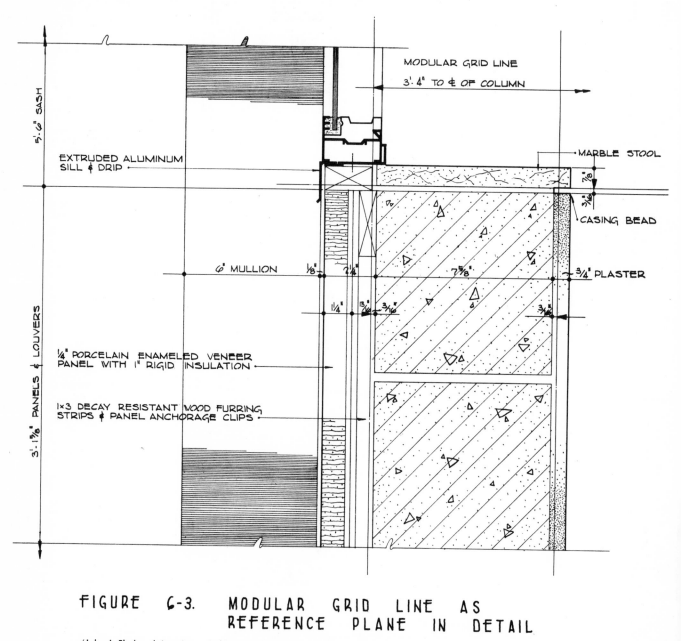

FIGURE 6-3.   MODULAR GRID LINE AS
REFERENCE PLANE IN DETAIL

(John J. Flad and Associates, Architects and Engineers, Madison, Wisconsin:
Wisland Corporation Apartment Building, Madison, Wisconsin)

The 4-inch grid on details.   The complete 4-inch modular grid is sometimes shown in detail drawings, as in Figures 6-6 and 6-7, to give a complete picture of the modular coordination of the parts.   As a general rule the inclusion of all grid lines is not necessary, since it complicates the reading of the detail and adds to the cost of drafting.   *For the sake of simplicity and clarity, excessive use of the grid is to be avoided.*

When the complete grid is shown on a detail, proper contrast between grid lines and detail lines is extremely important.   The confusion which results when grid lines are too heavy is shown, purposely exaggerated, in Figure 6-8.

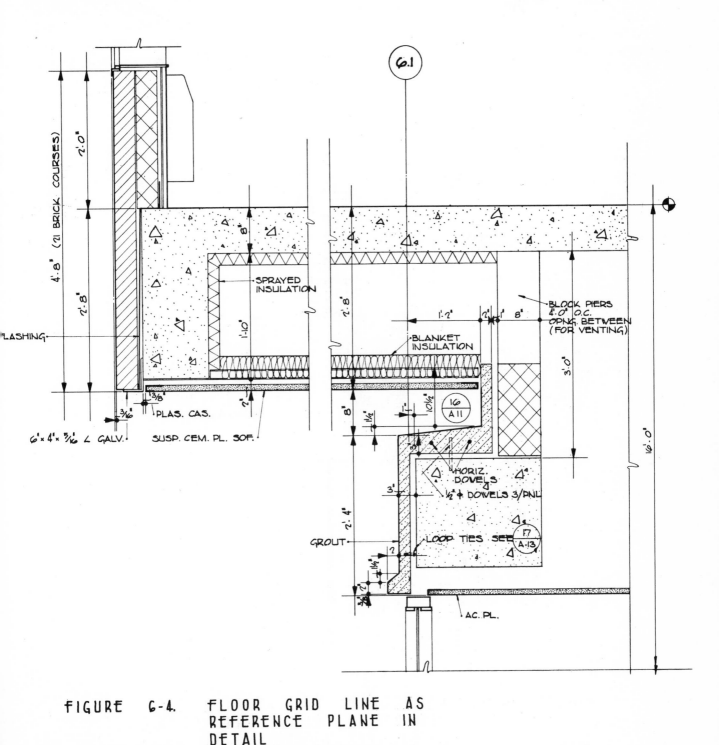

FIGURE 6-4.   FLOOR GRID LINE AS
REFERENCE PLANE IN
DETAIL

(Nolen and Swinburne, Architects, Philadelphia, Pennsylvania:
Men's Dormitories, Temple University, Philadelphia, Pennsylvania)

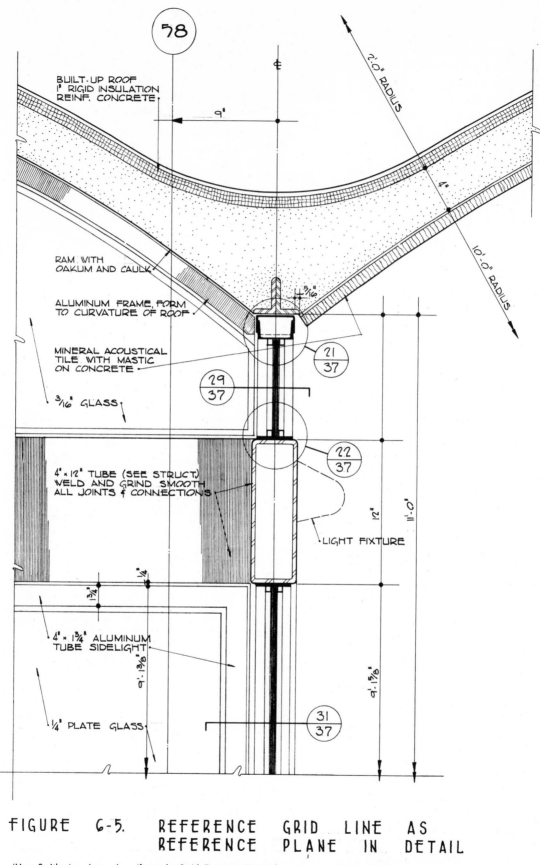

FIGURE 6-5.   REFERENCE GRID LINE AS
REFERENCE PLANE IN DETAIL

(Linn Smith Associates, Inc. (formerly Smith-Tarapata-MacMahon, Inc.), Architects–Engineers, Birmingham, Michigan: Wylie E. Groves High School, Birmingham, Michigan)

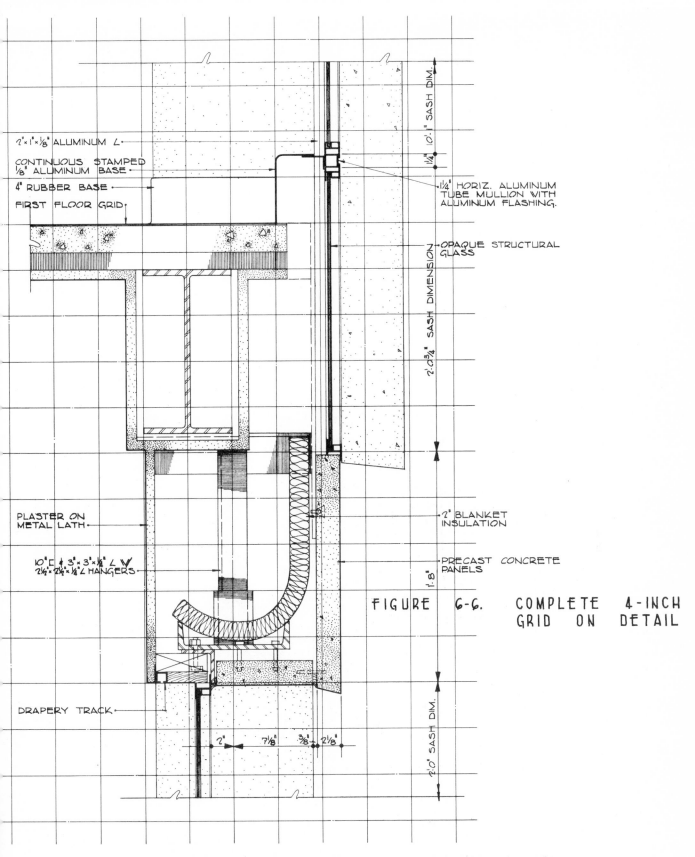

2"×1"×⅛" ALUMINUM ∟

CONTINUOUS STAMPED ⅛" ALUMINUM BASE

4" RUBBER BASE

FIRST FLOOR GRID

PLASTER ON METAL LATH

10" ⊏ & 3"×3"×¼" ∟ W 2½"×2½"×¼" ∟ HANGERS

DRAPERY TRACK

1¼" HORIZ. ALUMINUM TUBE MULLION WITH ALUMINUM FLASHING.

OPAQUE STRUCTURAL GLASS

2" BLANKET INSULATION

PRECAST CONCRETE PANELS

1¼" 10'-1" SASH DIM.

2'-0¾" SASH DIMENSION

1'-8"

2'-0" SASH DIM.

2"   7⅛"   ⅜"   2⅛"

FIGURE   6-6.   COMPLETE   4-INCH GRID   ON   DETAIL

(Linn Smith Associates, Inc. (formerly Smith-Tarapata-MacMahon, Inc.), Architects–Engineers, Birmingham, Michigan: Flint School District Administration Building, Flint, Michigan)

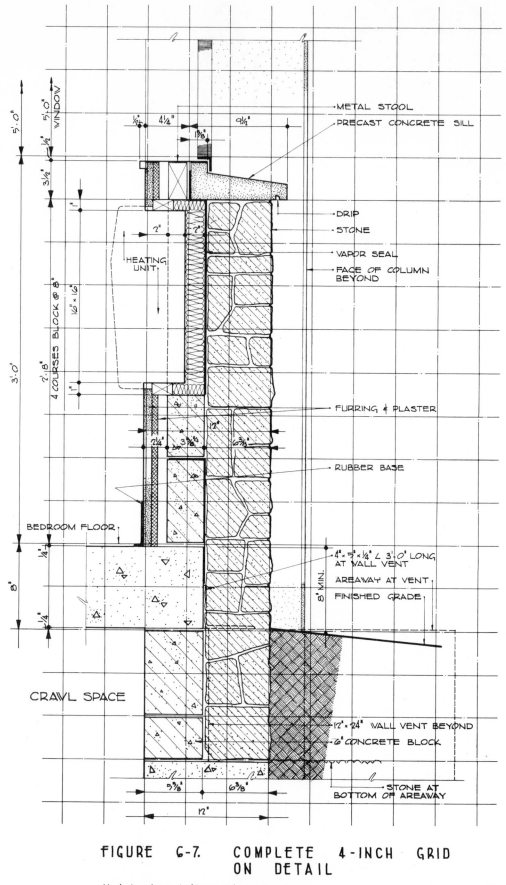

FIGURE 6-7.   COMPLETE   4-INCH   GRID
ON   DETAIL

(Aeck Associates, Architects, Atlanta, Georgia:
Girls' Dormitory, Tallulah Falls School, Tallulah Falls, Georgia)

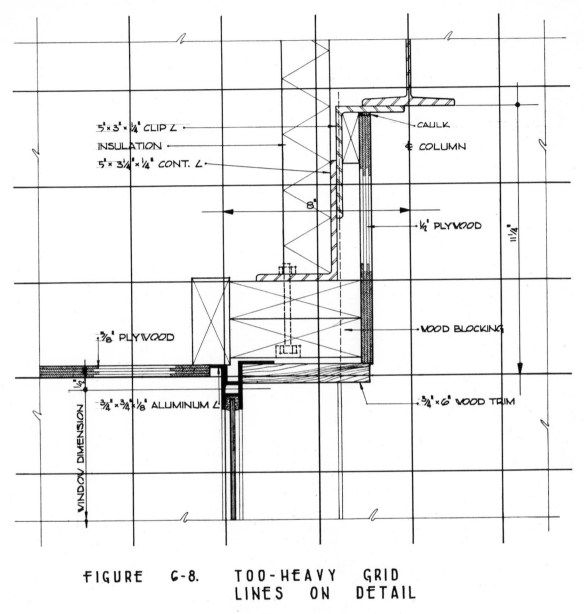

FIGURE   6-8.   TOO-HEAVY   GRID
LINES   ON   DETAIL

(Pederson, Hueber and Hares, Architects; Glavin, Landscape Architect, Syracuse, New York:
Westhill Junior-Senior High School, Onondaga County, New York)

Most architects prefer to indicate a minimum number of grid lines on details, showing only those which serve as reference lines for coordinating the details with other drawings, as illustrated in Figures 6-1 and 6-2. The improvement in clarity and simplicity with this approach is shown in Figure 6-9. This is the same detail which is illustrated in Figure 6-8, but it has been redrawn with a minimum of grid lines.

Nominal and actual faces. Dimensions may be given to nominal faces or to actual faces in large-scale details. There is no firm rule governing the

particular method of dimensioning to faces, and the architect should rely on his judgment to determine which method is best in a particular situation. Generally, true dimensions to actual faces are given on fabricated items, and these are located with reference to the modular grid. Two examples of dimensioning to actual faces are shown in Figures 6-10 and 6-11.

Joint center lines. Another method of dimensioning to nominal faces is to dimension to joint center lines. A specific example of the use of this method in large-scale details is shown in Figure 6-12. The

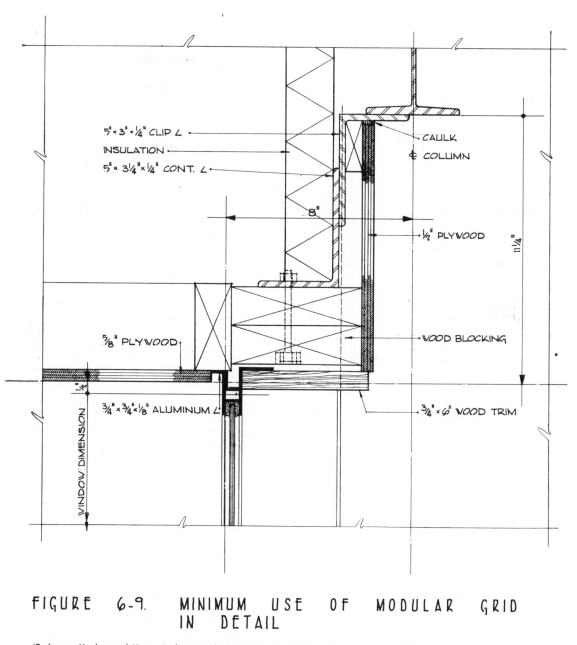

FIGURE   6-9.   MINIMUM   USE   OF   MODULAR   GRID
IN   DETAIL

(Pederson, Hueber and Hares, Architects; Glavin, Landscape Architect, Syracuse, New York:
Westhill Junior-Senior High School, Onondaga County, New York)

dimension to the center line of the joint is used also to establish a joist bearing location and to locate the wall fin radiator.

Reference and structural grid lines. Reference and structural grid lines which pass through a detail should be shown. They are important coordinate lines to which dimensions are given in plan, and thus they aid in coordinating the detail with the smaller-scale drawing, either plan or elevation, in which it occurs. Structural grid lines on a portion of a floor plan are shown in Figure 6-13 with the pertinent details in which the grid lines also appear.

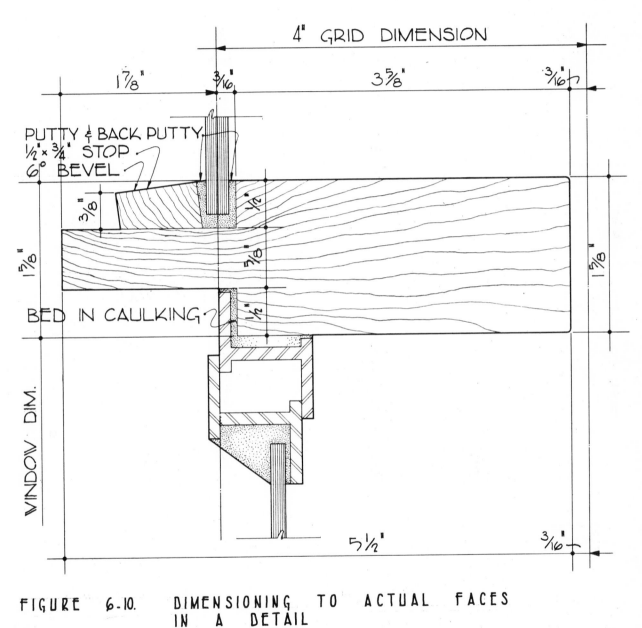

FIGURE 6-10.   DIMENSIONING TO ACTUAL FACES
IN A DETAIL

(Brown and Wright Associates, Architects, Washington, D. C.:
Bogounoff Residence, Langley, Virginia)

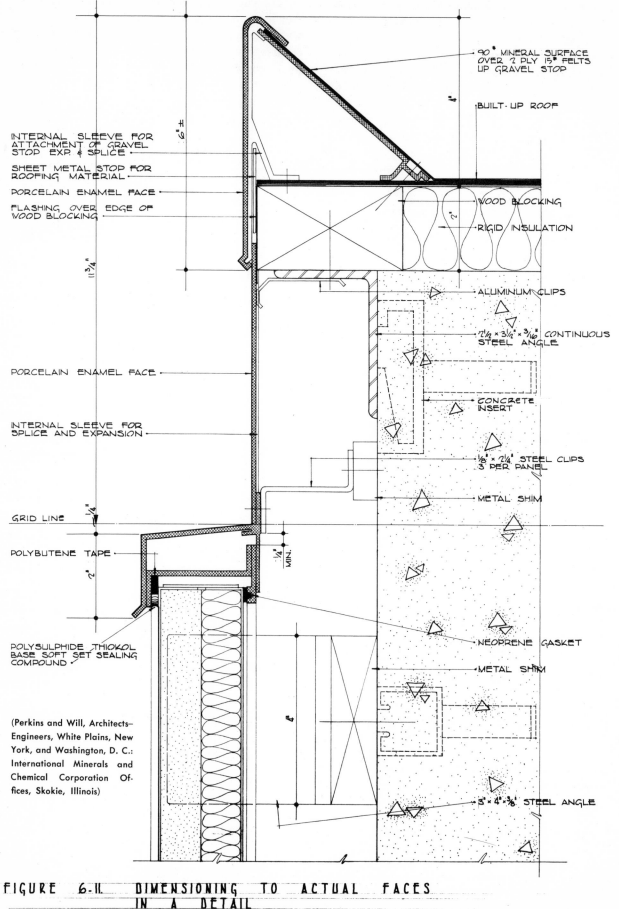

INTERNAL SLEEVE FOR
ATTACHMENT OF GRAVEL
STOP EXP. & SPLICE

SHEET METAL STOP FOR
ROOFING MATERIAL

PORCELAIN ENAMEL FACE

FLASHING OVER EDGE OF
WOOD BLOCKING

PORCELAIN ENAMEL FACE

INTERNAL SLEEVE FOR
SPLICE AND EXPANSION

GRID LINE

POLYBUTENE TAPE

POLYSULPHIDE THIOKOL
BASE SOFT SET SEALING
COMPOUND

(Perkins and Will, Architects–
Engineers, White Plains, New
York, and Washington, D. C.:
International Minerals and
Chemical Corporation Of-
fices, Skokie, Illinois)

90 # MINERAL SURFACE
OVER 2 PLY 15# FELTS
UP GRAVEL STOP

BUILT-UP ROOF

WOOD BLOCKING

RIGID INSULATION

ALUMINUM CLIPS

2½" × 3½" × 3/16" CONTINUOUS
STEEL ANGLE

CONCRETE
INSERT

1/8" × 2¼" STEEL CLIPS
3 PER PANEL

METAL SHIM

NEOPRENE GASKET

METAL SHIM

3" × 4" × 3/8" STEEL ANGLE

FIGURE   6-11.   DIMENSIONING   TO   ACTUAL   FACES
IN   A   DETAIL

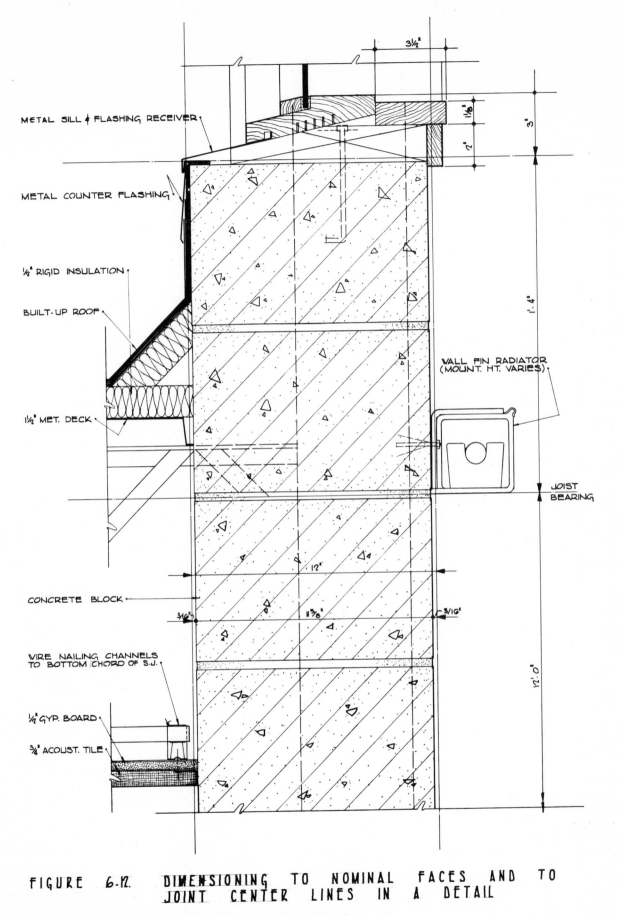

METAL SILL & FLASHING RECEIVER

METAL COUNTER FLASHING

½" RIGID INSULATION

BUILT-UP ROOF

1½" MET. DECK

CONCRETE BLOCK

WIRE NAILING CHANNELS
TO BOTTOM CHORD OF S.J.

½" GYP. BOARD

¾" ACOUST. TILE

3½"

1⅛"

3"

2"

1'-4"

WALL FIN RADIATOR
(MOUNT. HT. VARIES)

JOIST
BEARING

12"

3/16"

1⅜"

3/16"

12'-0"

FIGURE 6-12. DIMENSIONING TO NOMINAL FACES AND TO
JOINT CENTER LINES IN A DETAIL

(John J. Flad and Associates, Architects and Engineers, Madison, Wisconsin:
St. Maria Goretti Parish Center, Madison, Wisconsin)

121

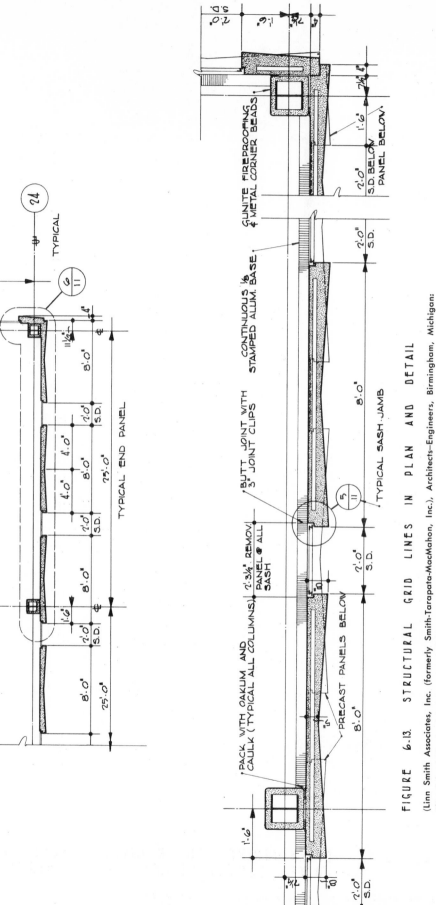

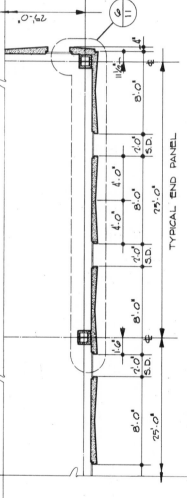

FIGURE 6.13. STRUCTURAL GRID LINES IN PLAN AND DETAIL

(Linn Smith Associates, Inc. (formerly Smith-Tarapata-MacMahon, Inc.), Architects-Engineers, Birmingham, Michigan: Flint School District Administration Building, Flint, Michigan)

Wylie E. Groves High School
Birmingham, Michigan

Linn Smith Associates, Inc.
(formerly Smith-Tarapata-MacMahon)
Architects—Engineers
Birmingham, Michigan

FUNCTION OF THE ENGINEERING DRAWINGS

A set of working drawings includes engineering drawings which complement the architectural drawings and delineate the structure and the electro-mechanical services of the building. These drawings show the location and size of the structural elements; the location, shape, and sizes of heating, ventilating, and air-conditioning equipment; and the location of the electrical distribution system, fixtures, and electrical equipment. They are coordinated with each other and with the architectural drawings to provide a complete and functional picture of the building. The scale of the engineering drawings usually corresponds with the scale of the architectural drawings.

STRUCTURAL DRAWINGS

The architectural and engineering aspects of any building project are closely interwoven and must be coordinated from the initial stages of a design project. In terms of modular design, there should be early collaboration between architect and engineer to develop the desirable coordination of plan, structure, and services. When the engineer understands the reasoning behind the selection of a planning grid, and is involved in the early discussions concerning structure, materials, and electro-mechanical systems, the development of the engineering drawings on a modular basis will proceed more rapidly.

There is a strong similarity between the modular dimensioning of structural drawings and that of architectural drawings. The structural grid drawn through columns in both types of drawings provides a positive reference system to which dimensions are taken and to which other elements of the building are related. Reference grids which are shown in the architectural drawings are used also in the structural drawings. The 4-inch modular grid serves as the means of expressing the modular coordination, and the arrow and dot dimensioning system as the technical device for relating the parts.

Steel. In steel structures, the members are seldom modular in size, and dimensions are usually given to column centers. Large-scale details of connections show the actual dimensions of the members and tie them to the modular grid by means of the modular-dimensioning system. Each individual column is not dimensioned on the structural plans, as the separate column schedule lists and locates each one.

Only the center lines of members other than columns are shown in floor and roof framing plans. If the center line of such a member is not on the center line of a column into which it frames, an

7
STRUCTURAL, MECHANICAL, AND ELECTRICAL

actual dimension is used to locate the two lines with respect to each other. Arrows and dots show whether or not they are also modular grid lines.

A structural floor plan for the building shown in Figure 4-12 is given in Figure 7-1. The structural grid is modular, and the few dimensions which are required all relate to this grid.

Architects and engineers agree that the dimensioning system should be consistent throughout a set of working drawings. If the architectural drawings are modular, the engineering drawings also should be as modular as possible.

Concrete. Structural concrete drawings are not always modular even though the concrete members are coordinated with other materials which are

modular. As a homogeneous material which is usually placed in forms on the job, concrete has no nominal size and has customarily been shown with actual dimensions. This is acceptable when the architectural drawings also show actual dimensions, even though both are unnecessarily full of fractional dimensions. However, when the architectural drawings are prepared with modular dimensions and the structural concrete drawings with actual dimensions, difficulties arise in cross checking between them. This problem can be avoided by the use of modular dimensions on concrete members, modular large-scale details, a modular note to the contractor on the structural drawings, and good supervision during construction.

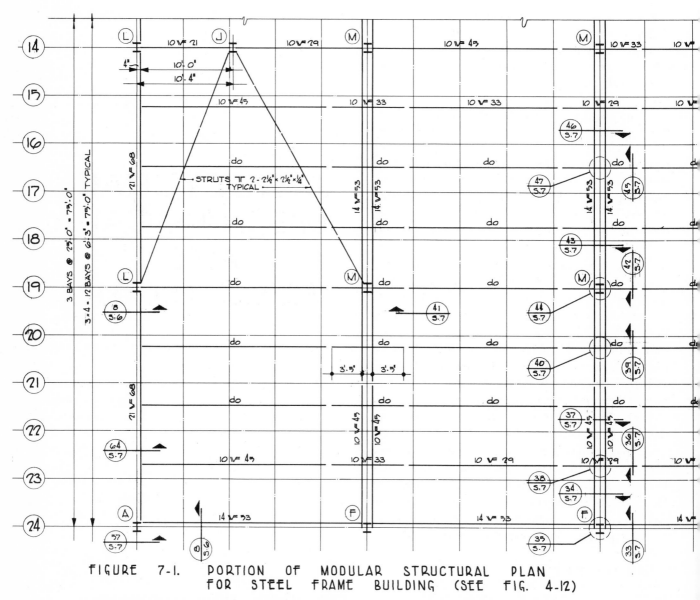

FIGURE 7-1. PORTION OF MODULAR STRUCTURAL PLAN
FOR STEEL FRAME BUILDING (SEE FIG. 4-12)

(Linn Smith Associates, Inc. (formerly Smith-Tarapata-MacMahon, Inc.), Architects–Engineers, Birmingham, Michigan:
Flint School District Administration Building, Flint, Michigan)

Another technique is valuable in relating the modular and the actual dimensions. It is particularly applicable to foundation plans. This is the addition of an actual size dimension adjacent to the nominal dimension. This technique does not require an additional string of actual dimensions through the foundation plan, but specifically points out the actual size of a wall, a footing, or a column to the man responsible for building the forms. The modular dimensions of the structural drawings thus correlate with those on the architectural drawings, facilitating the location of major elements and making for simpler cross checking. At the same time, there is no doubt as to the exact size of a given element and its relationship to the modular grid. Actual dimensions are given also in the large-scale details which show the size and placement of reinforcing steel.

Dimensions on structural concrete framing plans are modular and indicate nominal sizes of columns and beams. The actual sizes of these members are listed in the schedules, and there is no need to repeat them on the drawings.

Reference and structural grids are used on these drawings according to the judgment of the engineer. Good communication between architect and engineer will help them to coordinate their presentation techniques for the greatest clarity and the best means of reference.

A portion of the floor plan of a concrete-frame school and the accompanying structural framing plan are shown in Figures 7-5 and 7-6. A 3-foot reference grid is drawn on the floor plan, evenly dividing the 30-foot structural grid, but only the structural grid is shown on the engineering drawing. The 3-foot pans of the concrete floor, which coincide with the reference grid, are shown dotted on this drawing.

ELECTRICAL AND MECHANICAL DRAWINGS

The inherent discipline of modular practice may be applied to the development of electro-mechanical systems to achieve efficiency, economy, and quality just as in other phases of the building process. Electro-mechanical systems for the most part are concealed. The visible portions—air diffusers, lighting fixtures, switches, telephone outlets—are in the minority and are subject to the aesthetic coordination required by the architect. The concealed portions, however, are subject to a disciplined development which obviates much of the expense of individual shop-drawing production and transfers much of the fabrication to the shop from the site. For those projects in which repetitious elements are involved, savings in modular electromechanical construction are substantial.

Modular practice also provides the design flexibility which minimizes the electro-mechanical costs involved whenever a building undergoes spatial changes as a result of changing functions.

In addition, modular practice promulgates more efficient coordination between the structural engineer and the electro-mechanical engineer because of its discipline in space allocation and designation. The development of such items as air diffusion, sprinkler protection, drainage, and lighting intensity in terms of planning modules, rather than on a linear or square-foot basis, permits greater interchange of element capability. Through modular practice, the architect can maintain greater control and develop greater command of engineering systems to permit exploration of design concepts within practicable areas of system capability.

In many types of buildings, modular discipline helps to establish the vertical control which is necessary in floor-ceiling construction for the design of crossover of electro-mechanical systems. Floor-to-floor heights are affected by the depth required for air ducts, lighting system, and drainage system and must be carefully controlled in design. When these systems are established on a vertical control grid before floor-to-floor heights are set, the simplification and precision which result can lead to substantial economies.

Mechanical and electrical plans usually require few dimensions. Ducts, pipes, and wiring conduits are shown on a lightly drawn background of the architectural floor plan and are located with visual reference to walls, doors, shafts, and other elements of the plan. When a reference grid is used on the architectural plans, it should be shown also on the engineering drawings. Where dimensions are called for, reference is made to the modular grid.

In planning for the use of modular ducts, the mechanical engineer must take into consideration the difference between the nominal size and the amount of space required for clearance. The nominal size of a duct is its inside dimension. When thermal or acoustical insulation is applied to the outside of the duct, the thickness of flange and insulation on both sides must be added to the nominal dimension to determine the necessary clearance.

Mechanical and electrical drawings which accompany the structural drawing of the steel-frame building in Figure 7-1 are shown in Figures 7-2, 7-3, and 7-4. Dimensions are at a minimum, and location of the elements is largely determined by plotting on the floor plan and the reference grid.

Mechanical and electrical drawings for the concrete-frame school in Figure 7-5 are presented in Figures 7-7 and 7-8. These drawings from a single building demonstrate the small amount of dimen-

sioning which is required in engineering drawings, and show the influence of the structural and reference grids in maintaining dimensional order.

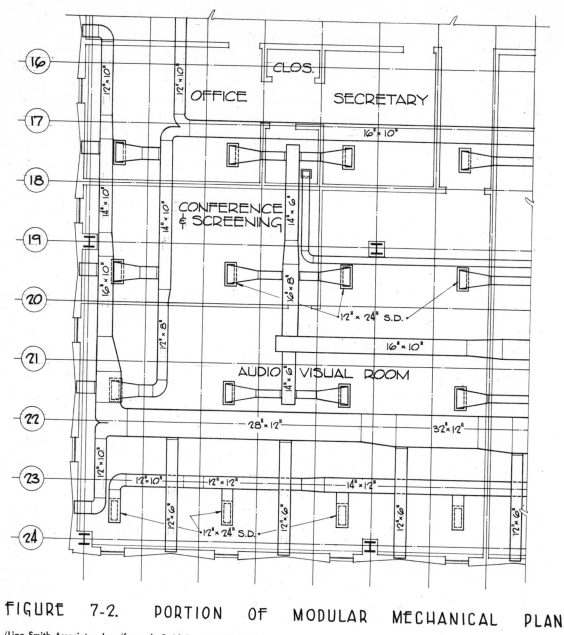

FIGURE 7-2.   PORTION OF MODULAR MECHANICAL PLAN

(Linn Smith Associates, Inc. (formerly Smith-Tarapata-MacMahon, Inc.), Architects–Engineers, Birmingham, Michigan: Flint School District Administration Building, Flint, Michigan)

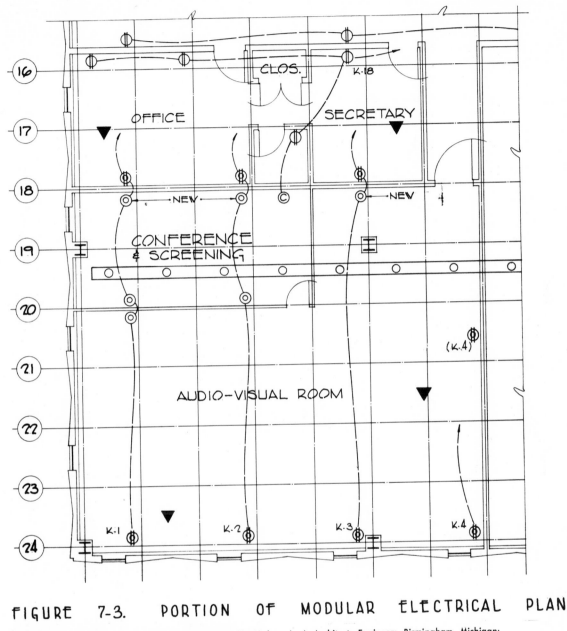

FIGURE 7-3.   PORTION OF MODULAR ELECTRICAL PLAN

(Linn Smith Associates, Inc. (formerly Smith-Tarapata-MacMahon, Inc.), Architects—Engineers, Birmingham, Michigan:
Flint School District Administration Building, Flint, Michigan)

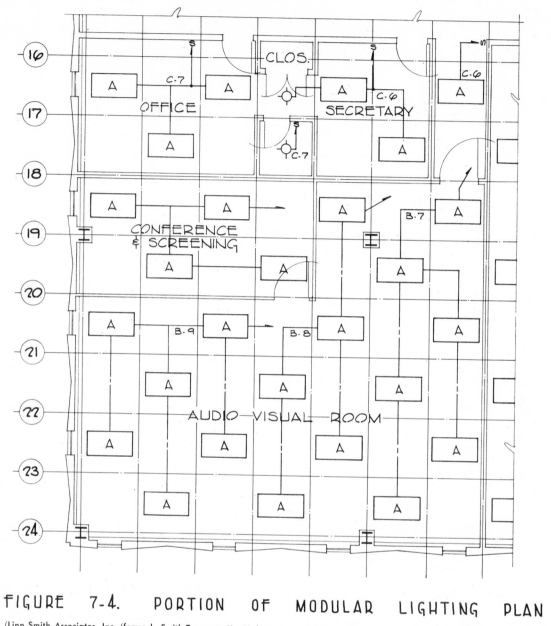

FIGURE 7-4.   PORTION OF MODULAR LIGHTING PLAN

(Linn Smith Associates, Inc. (formerly Smith-Tarapata-MacMahon, Inc.), Architects—Engineers, Birmingham, Michigan:
Flint School District Administration Building, Flint, Michigan)

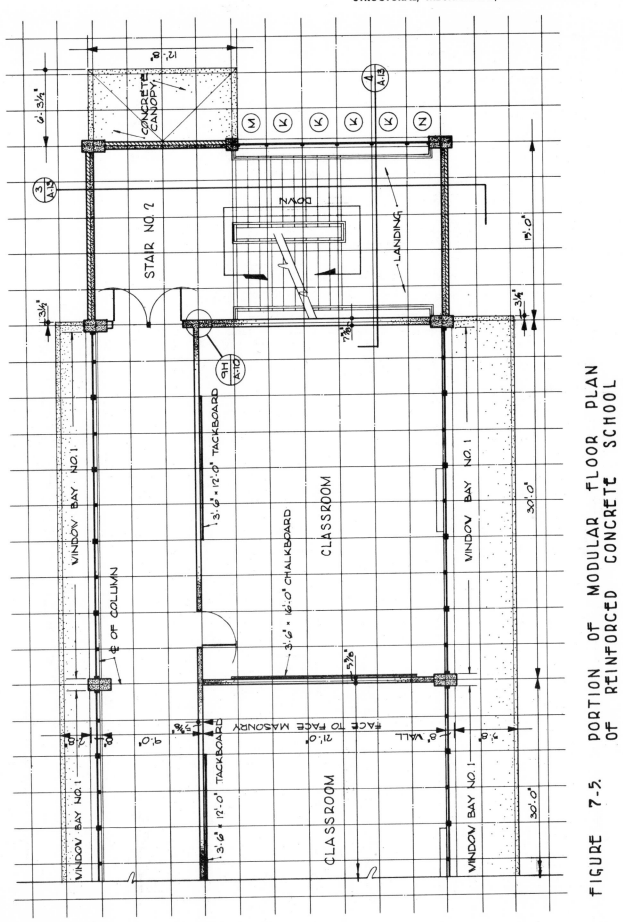

FIGURE 7-5.   PORTION OF MODULAR FLOOR PLAN OF REINFORCED CONCRETE SCHOOL

(Aeck Associates, Architects, Atlanta, Georgia:
Lovett School, Atlanta, Georgia)

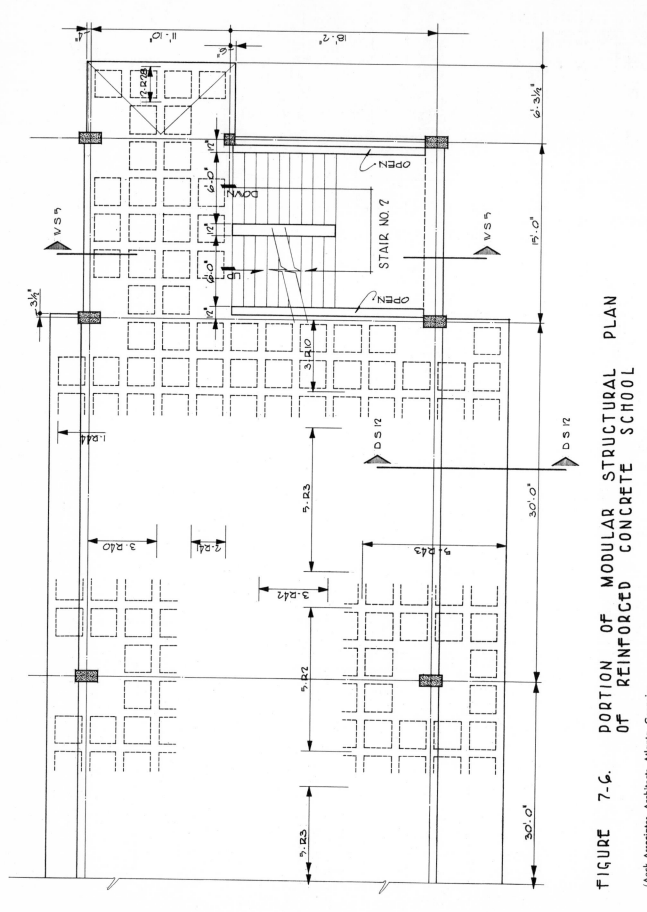

FIGURE 7-6.   PORTION OF MODULAR STRUCTURAL PLAN
OF REINFORCED CONCRETE SCHOOL

(Aeck Associates, Architects, Atlanta, Georgia:
Lovett School, Atlanta, Georgia)

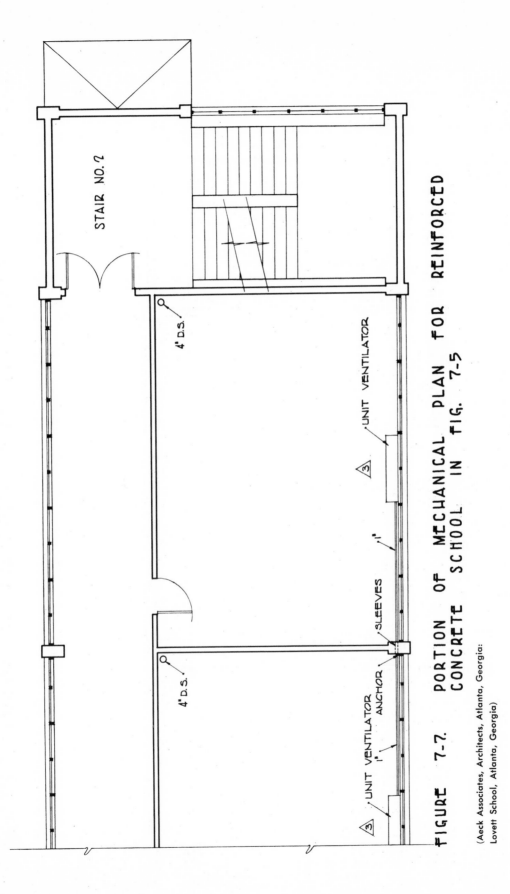

FIGURE 7-7. PORTION OF MECHANICAL PLAN FOR REINFORCED CONCRETE SCHOOL IN FIG. 7-5

(Aeck Associates, Architects, Atlanta, Georgia:
Lovett School, Atlanta, Georgia)

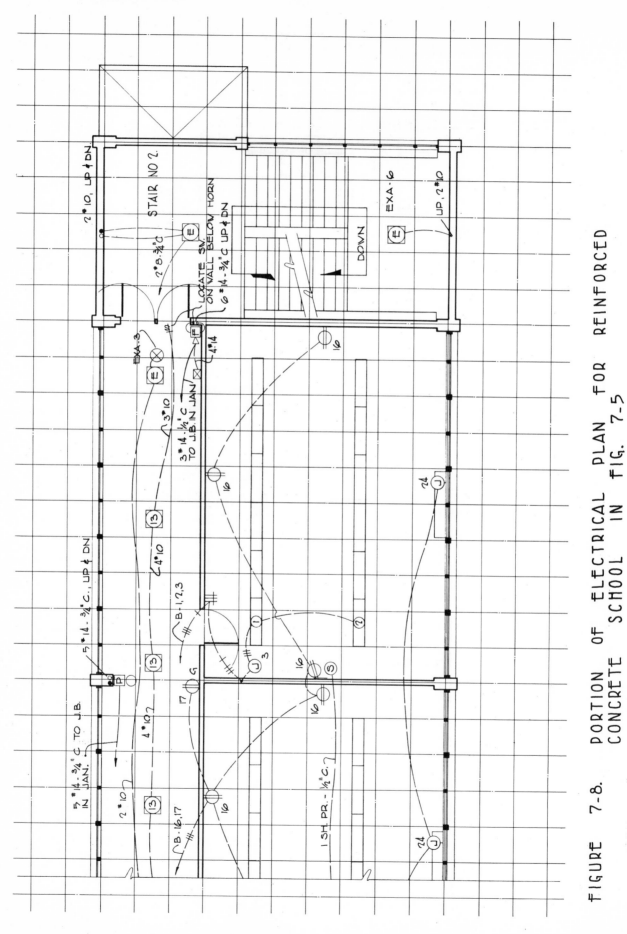

FIGURE 7-8.   PORTION OF ELECTRICAL PLAN FOR REINFORCED
CONCRETE SCHOOL IN FIG. 7-5

(Aeck Associates, Architects, Atlanta, Georgia:
Lovett School, Atlanta, Georgia.)

Temple University Medical Research Building
Philadelphia, Pennsylvania

Nolen and Swinburne
Architects
Philadelphia, Pennsylvania

BENEFITS TO CONTRACTOR

The building contractor, as a businessman, expects, and is entitled to, a reasonable profit for his services. Modular practice offers the contractor a number of benefits. It helps to reduce bidding time and to improve the quality of his work because the coordination of materials requires less cutting, fitting, and patching. By shortening the construction period, modular practice helps to lower overhead and other costs and enables the contractor to bid more competitively to provide better and less expensive school buildings.

BIDDING

Modular note and briefing session. A contractor, before bidding, should be advised by a note on the drawings that the project was designed on modular principles and that the drawings are modular. Several types of such notes were presented in Chapter 4. In addition to a note, some architects hold a briefing session before bidding for all the contractors who are not familiar with modular work. They explain the modular principles on which the building was designed and the construction techniques which can be used to take advantage of the modular design.

Simpler drawings. A contractor must allow time to familiarize himself with a project before he prepares a bid based on the drawings and specifications. He must study the plan, visit the site, and analyze the structural, electrical, and mechanical systems. The time required for this understanding of the project before bidding is often lengthy when the drawings contain many fractional dimensions, are not developed from a system of materials coordination, and lack a clear reference system for locating specific areas and items in the building. Conversely, with the simpler drawings which are developed for a modular building, the contractor's time is reduced substantially.

The difference in simplicity and clarity between a plan which is developed and dimensioned according to modular principles and one which is not is shown in Figures 8-1 and 8-2. The same plan is used in both illustrations. A comparison of the two drawings shows how easily the nonmodular plan could be made modular. Similar comparisons can be made between the fireplace sections in Figure 8-3, and between the large-scale details in Figure 8-4. The simplicity which is apparent in the modular examples will be seen in all the drawings of a building designed and dimensioned on modular principles.

Material take-off. Following his general orientation, the contractor or his estimator makes a labor

8

MODULAR PRACTICE AND THE CONTRACTOR

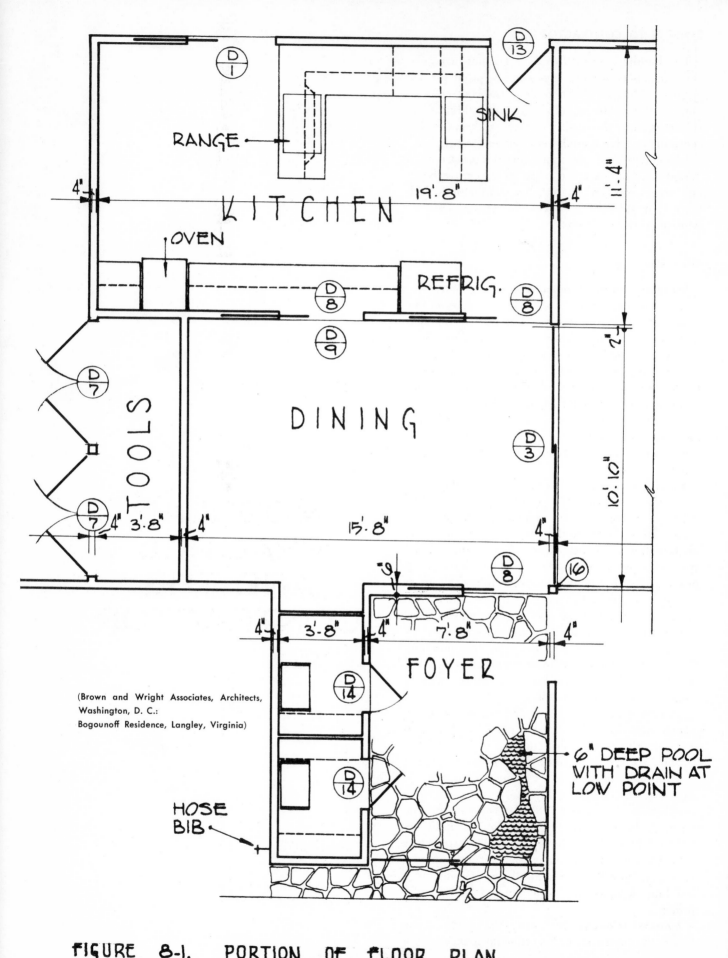

FIGURE 8-1. PORTION OF FLOOR PLAN WITH MODULAR DIMENSIONS

(Brown and Wright Associates, Architects, Washington, D. C.:
Bogounoff Residence, Langley, Virginia)

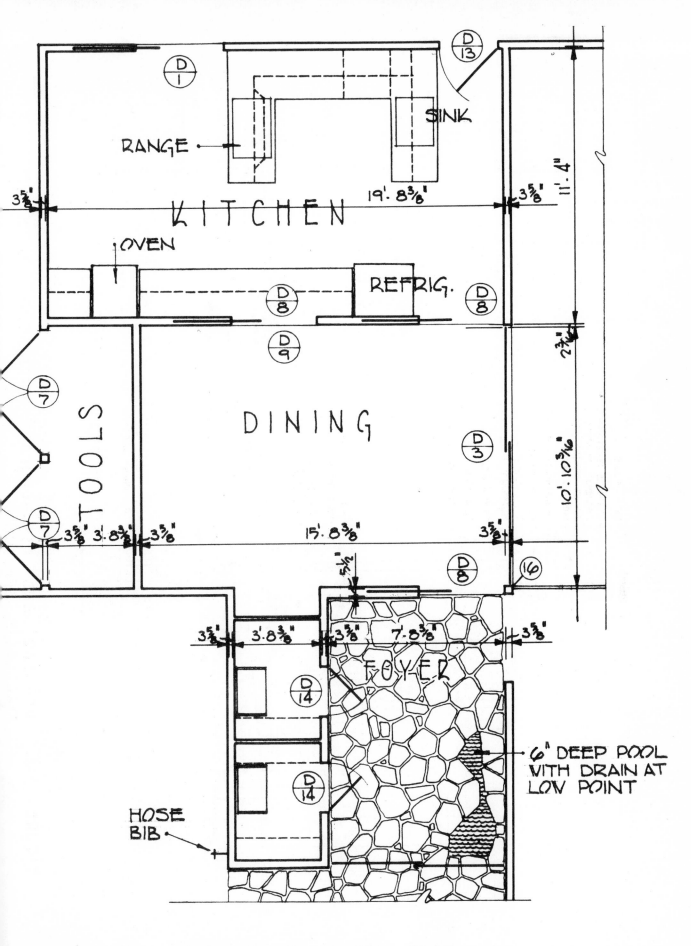

FIGURE 8-2. PORTION OF FLOOR PLAN
WITH NON-MODULAR DIMENSIONS

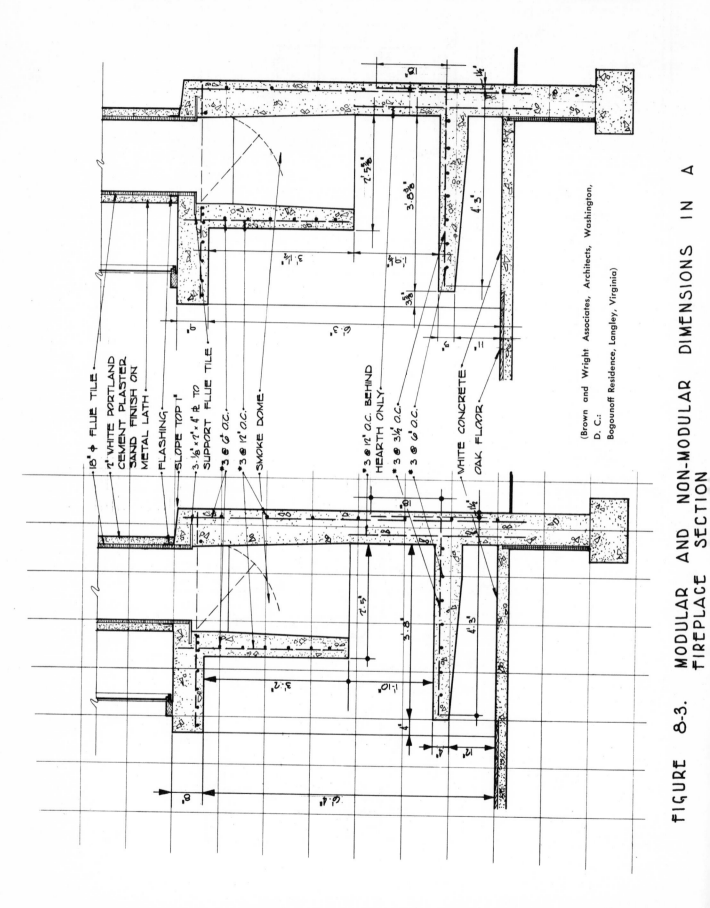

FIGURE 8-3.   MODULAR AND NON-MODULAR DIMENSIONS IN A
FIREPLACE SECTION

(Brown and Wright Associates, Architects, Washington,
D. C.:

Bogounoff Residence, Langley, Virginia)

and material take-off which he translates into the cost of materials and the labor cost of erecting them. Materials and areas which are sized in terms of multiples of a basic module are translated into total quantities more accurately than those with uncoordinated, fractional dimensions. The simple, nonfractional dimensions and the greater clarity of the drawings also make the material take-off quicker and easier. Reports from contractors with no previous experience with modular drawings indicate savings in take-off and bidding time of 25 to 50 per cent over the time which would have been required with nonmodular drawings.

Labor cost. The contractor who understands the application of modular dimensioning on the job in terms of reduced labor time can usually submit a lower bid. Reduction of labor time and of the in-place cost of materials results from the coordination which is an inherent part of a modular design. Ini-

tial layout is easier and quicker because of the simple dimensions and the reference grid, both of which reduce measuring time and measuring errors.

CONSTRUCTION

Pre-construction modular briefing. Many architects hold another briefing session for the successful contractor, the subcontractors, and their key men before the start of construction. This is done even if a similar session were held before bidding, because the subcontractors and foremen were not present at the first session. The architect explains again the modular principles and enlarges on the construction techniques with which the men might not be familiar. During construction, the architect follows up by assisting in the modular layout and in the interpretation of the drawings.

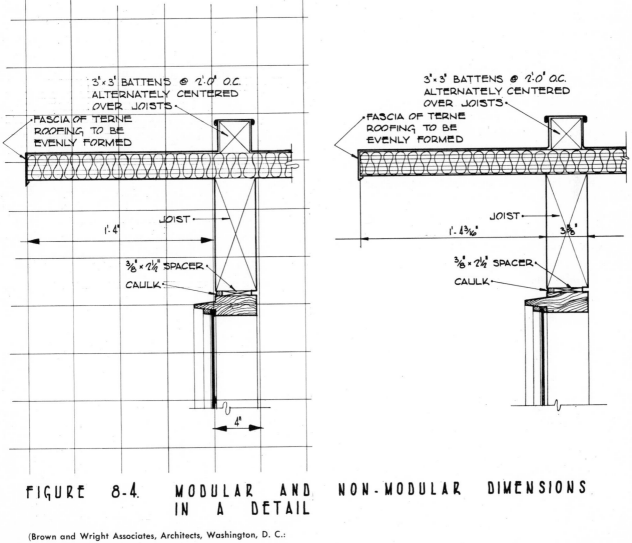

FIGURE 8-4.   MODULAR AND NON-MODULAR DIMENSIONS IN A DETAIL

(Brown and Wright Associates, Architects, Washington, D. C.: Bogounoff Residence, Langley, Virginia)

Grid lines on batter boards. Some contractors, building a modular project for the first time, experience difficulty with the modular-dimensioning system during construction. Their main problem lies in working to nominal faces and to grid lines instead of to actual faces, particularly at exterior walls. The grid lines are imaginary, and the contractors find it difficult to establish their location for measuring purposes by means of traditional building techniques. However, contractors who have worked with modular construction have developed a simple method of handling the grid lines which recognizes the presence of the grid during the initial layout of a building. They mark the grid line on the batter boards half a joint width outside the mark for the actual face of the foundation wall, and use this to establish check points within the building from which dimensions may be measured.

Modular check points. The establishing of check points is not a new idea, nor is the marking of batter boards; the only difference in modular construction is that the marks and check points represent grid lines. The check points always coincide with structural and reference grid lines for coordination and control. From the check points, modular dimensions to the various elements of the plan are laid out. Then grid lines are marked on floors or walls for guidance, and materials are placed with reference to these lines according to the dimensions on the working drawings.

Contractors who have erected buildings from modular drawings have found that the amount of required measuring is reduced. Their major concern is the accurate location of grid lines. Modular tapes and rules designed specifically for use with the 4-inch module facilitate accurate measuring.

Construction benefits. *Layout is quicker and more accurate when the drawings have nonfractional dimensions and when reference and structural grids are used for control.* The workman who is familiar with modular construction often can place materials with less use of his rule by employing a grid line as a guide. Cutting, fitting, and patching are held to a minimum because of the design coordination of modular units and components, and there is less resultant waste. Finally, the gradual accumulation of dimensional errors is almost eliminated by the use of the modular grid. A deviation in the size of a component, or a tendency on the part of a workman to make a wider joint than called for, will become noticeable by reference to the grid, and can be corrected or compensated for immediately by continuing to place materials according to the grid and absorbing the variations in the joints.

SUPERVISION

Aids to supervision. Supervision by both architect and contractor is simpler on a modular project. The nonfractional dimensions result in less confusion and fewer questions, and telephone discussion of specific areas is facilitated by use of the reference grid. Fewer on-the-job decisions are required because of the coordination of materials, which leads to better workmanship and a higher quality in the finished product.

Tolerances are provided in all types of construction, and normal accuracy is all that is required for efficient modular construction. In general, the more accurate the construction, the better modular coordination will work. For this reason, close supervision of layout, and the accurate location of check points and structural and reference grids, pay dividends in the later stages of construction, as modular materials can be placed with a minimum of effort when the basic layout of the building has been done accurately.

Lansing Elementary School
Ludlowville, New York

Sargent, Webster, Crenshaw and Folley
Architects and Engineers
Syracuse, New York

Manufacturers as well as owners, architects, and contractors have a stake in modular practice. The specification of modular products by architects, and increasing familiarity with the techniques of modular construction on the part of contractors, are creating an expanding market for products whose size and jointing characteristics are based on the requirements of modular coordination. A basic aim of coordination in building is to eliminate waste and confusion. The production of modular materials can lessen the chaotic building-material situation by substantially reducing the number of stock sizes which must be carried. This will lead to increased use of modular materials by architects and reduce the requests for special sizes. An example is the almost complete acceptance of concrete block in modular sizes.

Modular practice does not preclude the use of nonmodular materials. Structural, reference, and modular grids are effective means of communicating building coordination regardless of the materials used. Some additional cutting and fitting may be required if nonmodular materials are used, but this extra work can be minimized through careful study of sizes and dimensions during the design of the building. Coordination is simpler and more complete, however, if the total scope of modular practice is employed.

THE MANUFACTURERS' PROBLEMS

Limit dimensions and tolerances. The introduction of new materials or new sizes always presents problems for the manufacturer. One of the most important and critical problems in the development of modular materials is the establishing of limit dimensions and tolerances. Architectural planning for the use of materials and components manufactured to meet modular-dimensional specifications is based on their jointing and installation characteristics. This requires that in the design and sizing of a modular material the manufacturer must establish the limiting dimensions of the product and the workable tolerances of both product size and joint size. The guides he must follow are the basic concepts of modular coordination and several definitions * and diagrams * involved in modular practice and the sizing of modular components.

Standard modular space grid. A reference space grid with planes spaced at the standard module of 4 inches.

Standard modular component. A building component of standardized or specified dimensions which, when

* S. R. Kent, *The Sizing of Modular Components,* Technical Bulletin 87, The Producers' Council, Inc., March, 1959, pp. 28, 54: a reprint of Building Note 36, Division of Building Research, National Research Council of Canada.

9

MANUFACTURING FOR MODULAR

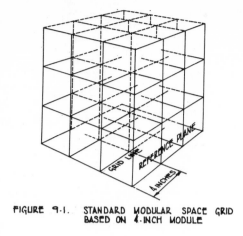

FIGURE 9-1.   STANDARD MODULAR SPACE GRID
BASED ON 4-INCH MODULE

used with its joint, fits the standard modular space grid.

Manufacture dimension.   A dimension of a component which is the manufacturer's catalogue dimension. It may deviate within specified limits due to uncontrollable factors in manufacture. This dimension is set out on the drawing with the understanding that deviations will be taken up by the joint.

Standard modular dimension.   (a) A dimension which used once or repeatedly is a multiple of the standard module of 4 inches; (b) the sum of a manufacture dimension and a joint.

Deviation.   The difference between an actual dimension and the corresponding manufacture dimension. This difference may be positive, negative, or zero.

Limit dimensions.   The maximum permitted oversize dimension (upper limit), or undersize dimension (lower limit), relative to the manufacture dimension.

Tolerance.   The difference between the permitted oversize (upper limit) and the permitted undersize (lower limit).

The standard modular space grid based on the 4-inch module is illustrated in Figure 9-1, and the concepts in the definitions above are presented in graphic form in Figure 9-2.

The sizing of a modular component based on these definitions is governed first by the standard modular space grid. Thus the dimensions of the component are multiples of 4 inches, such as 8 by 8 by 16 inches, or fit a multiple of 4 inches when regularly repeated, such as $2\frac{2}{3}$ by 4 by 12 inches. This is not necessarily true of the thickness of a component, as may be seen in a number of the illustrations in this book. Several examples are seen in Figures 4-10, 4-13, 5-15, and 6-13. Basically, the reason is that the thickness of materials is not built up of multiples. Modular dimensioning positions a material of x thickness wherever the architect desires, and there are too many potential thicknesses which are controlled by other factors to be involved in the system.

The modular dimension of a component includes the size of the component and its joint. Therefore, the component size and joint size must be worked out together so that the sum does not exceed the modular dimension. After determining the desirable modular size for a component, the manufacturer establishes the desirable joint size and fixes the manufacture dimension. Next he studies the feasibility of maintaining the manufacture size during production of the component, ascertains the probable deviations, and establishes the limits of deviation which are consistent with quality production. The allowable minimum and maximum joint limits are determined at this point because the joint will decrease as the manufacture dimension increases and will increase as the manufacture dimension decreases. This enables the over-all modular dimension to remain constant, as it must if there is to be no "creep" with relation to the modular space grid. Therefore, the maximum and minimum sizes of the component itself must be such as not to narrow or widen the joint beyond practicable limits. These factors establish the limits of size within which the component must be manufactured, and the limits of joint size which may be used in construction.

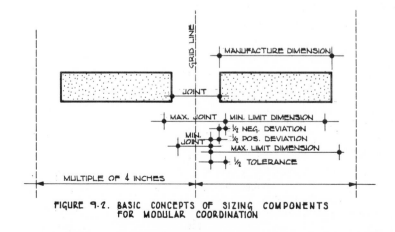

FIGURE 9-2. BASIC CONCEPTS OF SIZING COMPONENTS
FOR MODULAR COORDINATION

Coordinated and preferred sizes. One of the desirable goals of producing modular materials and components is the production of a minimum number of stock sizes which still allow the architect freedom in his solution of design requirements. Through careful study a minimum number of modular sizes can be coordinated to provide a wide range of flexibility. This has been done partially by analyzing past orders for materials or components to determine those sizes which are used most frequently in actual construction, based on selection by architects and builders. These sizes are then worked out in more detail in accordance with a preferred or additive numbers system. Short analyses of two such approaches are presented in Appendix C and Appendix D. The coordination of sizes should include coordination with a wide range of other materials and components as well as with units of the same type, and should include compatibility with a variety of planning modules. Preferred sizes are a logical means of conversion to modular sizes and to a smaller inventory of sizes.

Size determination. A number of physical problems face a manufacturer in the conversion to modular products. These are typical of any change in manufacturing processes and are not peculiar to modular products. In particular, the size or sizes of a product to be produced are dependent on a number of factors:

1. The size of machine or other required equipment which is available or can be provided.

2. The nature of the material itself. What will it stand in handling, either manually or by machine?

3. Manufacturer's storage space and handling facilities.

4. The limitations of transportation facilities, rail, truck, or air.

5. Job storage space and handling facilities.

6. The requirements of job assembly, whether manual or by machine.

Type of product. The type of product itself has implications of size selection in terms of how many

sizes are required. Some products are manufactured in only one or two modular sizes; others require several dozen or more. Some require coordination only in over-all modular size with other products, whereas some must incorporate other products, such as mechanical and electrical equipment, in their form during production.

Aesthetic influences such as various proportion theories (Appendix F) are a final manufacturing consideration which can lead to concentration on some sizes and to the rejection of others.

The progress which has been made in recent years in the conversion of several categories of building products to modular sizes is shown in Figure 9-3. Some are nearly 100 per cent modular, and there are no major categories of building materials in which modular products are not available.

Year		Estimated Percentage of Modular Production
1946–1950	Concrete masonry units (brick, block, decorative, and miscellaneous)	99
1948–1960	Windows (wood, steel, aluminum)	65
1961	Steel doors	5
1948–1960	Clay masonry units (brick, structural tile, glazed tile, miscellaneous)	50
1950–1960	Rolled sheet siding and roofing materials (steel, aluminum, plastic)	95
1950–1960	Precast structural units (floors, decking, etc.)	95
1950–1960	Movable partitions	75
1950–1960	Ceiling materials (including integrated lighting and mechanical fixtures)	95
1950–1960	Miscellaneous items (access doors, fireplace hardware, flue liners, window-wall systems, glass block, etc.)	5–100

FIGURE 9-3. PROGRESS OF CONVERSION OF BUILDING PRODUCTS TO MODULAR SIZES

Herrick Iron Works Administration Building
Hayward, California

John Carl Warnecke and Associates
Architects and Planning Consultants
San Francisco, California

Research, standards, education: these three areas in particular require concentrated study in relation to the future of modular practice. All are involved in the demands of the steadily enlarging school construction program, which require constant improvement in the efficiency of the building industry.

RESEARCH

Modular practice will expand as more modular materials become available in all parts of the country. Many of these involve research which must be carried out on a continuing basis to provide coordination of materials and construction systems. Research concerning the materials themselves is of basic importance because modular coordination requires materials of established and controlled sizes which will work within the discipline of the modular grid. The size of a product and the size and character of the joint connecting it with adjoining products can be established by research on the expansion and contraction characteristics of materials. The results of this research are important in determining allowable tolerances within the limits of the control possible in production.

Similar research is necessary with regard to components. *Component* is defined in the Canadian Standards Association's A31-1959 Code for Modular Coordination in Building as a "building material manufactured in a form for which certain dimensions are specified; the form may be a section, unit, or assembly." *Section, unit,* and *assembly* are further defined as follows:

Section. A building material produced in semifinished form, usually manufactured by a continuous process, of definite cross section and unspecified length, e.g., rolled, drawn, extruded, or sawn products such as steel shapes, tubes, pipes, planks, wallboard, wire and cable, sheet and plate, sawn boards.

Unit. A building material produced in finished form and of specified dimensions, e.g., concrete block, brick, structural tile, glass block.

Assembly. An arrangement of building units and sections to make a whole, e.g., door and frame, window, steel cabinets.

Large components are generally cheaper to produce and to erect than small ones, but have the disadvantage of restricting design freedom. They also pose more of a problem in control of expansion and contraction. However, this control must be achieved if the components are to be uniform enough in size and performance to be used in modular construction. Size research on components has been done mostly on the basis of the 4-inch module, and future efforts will expand the number of components which are sized to fit into the 4-inch modular concept.

10
THE FUTURE

A frequent design requirement, which necessitates dimensional stability, is interchangeability of components. Dimensional stability is demanded, also, by the fact that many components are prefabricated, are delivered as finished units, and cannot be cut to fit on the job. The sizes of a given type of component are dependent on the control possible in the manufacturing process and in maintaining the manufactured size within specified limits. If a component is too large to be contained within the required tolerances because of its expansion and contraction characteristics, it must be produced in a smaller size with less potential change in dimension.

Construction research is complementary to material and component research. Joints in buildings are a constant problem for architects and builders. The fewer the joints, the fewer the potential air and water leaks. But joints must be provided to take care of the inevitable movement of materials as they expand and contract because of moisture and temperature changes. Also, there are economic limits on the maximum sizes of materials and components in manufacturing, in shipping, and in handling on the job. New construction systems and new materials and components require constant research into new methods of jointing, and the jointing problem is tied directly to the use of larger sizes and to expansion and contraction characteristics. Standards of material and component tolerances will not be so rigid if joint systems and joint materials can be developed through research to handle large movements satisfactorily. But if joints continue to be limited in their capabilities, even more attention must be concentrated on materials and components.

Joints must be developed which allow interchangeability of materials and components of different types as well as like types, and which handle the joining of materials of different characteristics. The degree of success in the development of joints will affect the development of types and sizes of the building products themselves.

Research in materials, components, and construction methods will undoubtedly continue whether it is directed at modular coordination or not. But progress toward developing more efficient, labor-saving design and construction practices will be much more rapid if the building industry works as a whole toward the development of coordinated materials and construction techniques. The modular method offers these advantages, and future efforts in this direction will benefit all branches of the building industry.

A different type of research is called for in selecting for manufacture the specific range of sizes of materials and components. A smaller inventory of sizes is one of the benefits offered by a modular system. But freedom of design requires flexibility, and this must be provided by a carefully selected range of sizes which offers economy of inventory to the manufacturer and little or no restriction to the architect. This size-range research is largely mathematical and involves consideration of the degree of flexibility desired as well as preferred sizes, aesthetic factors, and factors of economy in production and construction. Two projects which are concerned with the selection of preferred sizes, modules, and maximum flexibility are presented in Appendix C and Appendix D. Both of the systems under consideration are compatible with the 4-inch modular system. The 4-inch system itself offers a high degree of flexibility in the design stage, as the development of modular dimensions never requires that a wall, a door, a window, or any other element be moved more than 2 inches to coincide with a grid line. With a selected range of sizes in modular materials which can be combined for dimensional flexibility, there should be little need for special orders or for cutting materials on the job.

STANDARDS

Standards for modular materials are being developed as the characteristics of the materials become defined. Interest concerning standards exists in many countries, and work has been under way for a number of years in Europe as well as in the United States and Canada in the study of standards and the problems of their international acceptance and adoption. In 1942, France issued the first national modular standard. The American Standards Association brought out standards on coordination of dimensions of building materials and equipment in 1945. A year later the Swedish Standards Association produced a thorough study on modular coordination, and similar standards were published by Belgium and Italy in 1948 and 1949. In the United Kingdom, the British Standards Institution and the Building Research Station have put much time and energy into building-coordination work. Since 1954 the European Productivity Agency Project on Modular Coordination (Appendix A) has sought to develop and establish international standards. Extension of this work will be carried on by the standards groups of the individual countries in collaboration with the International Standards Organization.

Study in the development of modular standards follows the line of establishing desirable modular goals for the building industry, determining and performing modular research, evaluating the results of the research, and recommending national and, if possible, international standards. The recommended standards deal with methods of determining tolerances and with the principles of selecting preferred sizes of materials and components.

One additional field for modular-standards study is that of products which are produced primarily for use in buildings but are subject to standards other than those of the building industry. Heating, plumbing, and electrical equipment fall into this category. Greater progress toward complete modular coordination will be made when products in these classifications are sized according to modular principles.

EDUCATION

A strong program of instruction in modular practice is necessary in colleges and universities to guarantee further development of modular design and construction. In architectural schools the relationship between modular design, modular coordination, and modular dimensioning should be stressed with a close tie between the courses in design and working drawings. The program should also include instruction in modular practice for students in the various branches of engineering and in construction management. A necessary complement to the program is the development of technical reference material illustrating the practical application of principles. This material would be of equal value in architectural offices and in schools. Through educational programs, the building industry will gradually acquire people with a basic understanding of modular practice and its importance as an essential part of the building process from design to construction.

This widespread understanding of modular practice will guarantee continuing support for the existing bodies which are studying and developing standards for the building industry. These include groups representing the separate professions and trades as well as the organizations which represent all interests, such as the American Standards Asso-

ciation and the Modular Buildin̦ ciation. The continuing work of will ensure constant development of applying modular principles in pr

THE CHALLENGE

The task facing the building industry iṣ ous. With regard to school-building consṭ the continuing population increase is produ_ing a constant pressure for more and more facilities. New techniques in the production and erection of building materials enable the industry to continue to keep pace with the demands, but the search for continued improvement cannot be abandoned. Modular practice, as outlined in this book, offers a major approach to the problem of providing an adequate number of all types of buildings, not only schools. But the school-building problem is one of the most pressing, and it is here that modular practice can demonstrate its value.

Changing educational requirements necessitate new or different facilities. Existing school buildings are often changed only with great difficulty to provide a new type of space. The ability of the architect and his educational consultants to foresee developments beyond a few years is necessarily limited, and new means of providing flexibility in school buildings are constantly being sought. Modular practice can play a significant part in the retarding of obsolescence in schools by providing the flexibility for easier change, replacement, and addition to meet unforeseen developments. Through the development of preferred sizes and stock components, it can lead to school buildings of lower cost with no lessening of design freedom for the architect, and thus provide a powerful answer to the sterility of stock plans for schools.

Widespread development and use of modular practice require concentrated efforts in modular research, the development of modular standards, instruction in modular practice in colleges and universities, and the organization and dissemination of modular information. As these efforts take effect, the result will be an increase in efficiency of design and in the quantity and quality of construction.

DEFINITIONS
OF
TERMS

ACTUAL CLEARANCE

The actual measurement of the joint or opening between two assembled parts.

ACTUAL DEVIATION

The difference between an actual measurement and the corresponding nominal measurement. This difference may be positive, negative, or zero.

ACTUAL DIMENSION

The dimension of a component taken after completion by direct measurement.

BASIC MODULE

(a) The fundamental module whose value is fixed to coordinate the sizes of components with the greatest flexibility and convenience. (b) A unit of measure. (c) A numerical coefficient.

BUILDING STANDARD

A standard concerned with building material, operations, functional requirements, or method of assembly.

CLEARANCE

The joint or opening (together for the two sides) between two assembled parts.

COMPONENTS

Building material manufactured in a form for which certain dimensions are specified: sections, units, and assemblies.

COORDINATING DIMENSION

Those measurements of a component determining the coordination of one component with another.

DEVIATION

The difference between an actual dimension and the corresponding manufacture dimension. This difference may be positive, negative, or zero.

DIMENSION

(a) The measurement of a body in one or more directions, e.g., in height, width, or length. (b) The distance between two lines or surfaces. (c) The value of such sizes expressed in terms of a unit of measure.

DIMENSIONAL COORDINATION

The organizing of dimensions to enable components to be used together without modification.

DIMENSIONAL STANDARD

A standard defining dimensions.

GRID LINE

A line in a reference grid, usually a line in a standard modular grid.

INCREMENT

The difference between two similarly located dimensions of components of successive size.

JOINT

(a) The space between two components. (b) Material which may occupy such a space.

Note: The desirable minimum and maximum joint dimensions shall be established in conjunction with the upper and lower limit dimensions.

LIMIT DIMENSIONS

The maximum permitted oversize dimension (upper limit), or undersize dimension (lower limit), relative to the manufacture dimension.

LOCATION DEVIATION

A tolerance for the positioning of a component.

LOWER DEVIATION

The difference between a lower limit (measurement) and the corresponding nominal measurement. This difference may be positive, negative, or zero.

MANUFACTURE DIMENSION

A dimension of a modular component which is the manufacturer's catalogue dimension. It may deviate within specified limits because of uncontrollable factors in manufacture. The manufacture dimension is set out on a drawing with the understanding that deviations will be taken up by the joint as shown on the modular detail.

MAXIMUM CLEARANCE

The greatest permissible total clearance which under the influence of the magnitude and location of the tolerances of two mating parts will occur between the two parts.

MEASUREMENT

The numerical expression of a dimension in terms of a given unit of measure which is set out on a drawing or which can be established by measuring an object.

MINIMUM CLEARANCE

The smallest permissible total clearance which under the influence of the magnitude and location of the tolerance of two mating parts will occur between the two parts.

MODULAR BUILDING

A system of building whose constituent components are wholly or partially modulated.

MODULAR COORDINATION

A system of dimensional coordination using the standard modular space grid of 4 inches.

MODULAR INCREMENT

Increment expressed as a multiple of the basic module.

MODULAR LINE

A reference line in a modular reference system.

MODULAR PLANE

A reference plane in a modular reference system.

MODULAR POINT

A reference point in a modular reference system.

MODULAR PRODUCTS

A component whose linkage dimensions are fixed on a modular basis without necessarily having modular measurements.

MODULAR SIZE

A multiple of the basic module.

MODULAR SPACE

A space allocated to a component which is bounded by its modular planes. (The size of a modular space is of the same modular order as that of its component.)

MODULAR SURFACE

A real or imaginary surface which coincides with a modular plane.

MODULAR SYSTEM

A system of rules for the use of a module to coordinate the design of a building and dimensions of building materials and equipment.

MODULAR VOLUME

A volume, the surfaces of which coincide with modular planes.

MODULATE

To use for linkage measurements of buildings, building components, etc., measurements which are based on a module or referred to a modular reference system.

MODULE

A common unit of measure particularly specified for dimensional coordination.

NOMINAL DIMENSION

The dimension which is used to designate the size of a component and which may differ from the corresponding actual dimension, e.g., a 2-inch by 4-inch wood stud.

PERMISSIBLE DEVIATION

The greatest permissible difference between an actual measurement and the corresponding nominal measurement. This difference may be positive, negative, or zero.

PLANNING GRID

A reference grid used for the preparation of plans and elevations of buildings. The grid is usually rectangular and has dimensions which are multiples of 4 inches. The spacing of the grid should be determined by the size of a standard modular component.

REFERENCE GRID

(a) A grid on a reference plane. (b) A network of lines from which the measurements and the position of building components may be determined.

REFERENCE LINE

A line to which reference can be made.

REFERENCE PLANE

A plane to which reference can be made, a plane of reference passing through a reference line.

REFERENCE POINT

A point to which reference can be made.

REFERENCE SPACE GRID

A three-dimensional system of reference planes.

REFERENCE SYSTEM

A system of lines, points, and planes from which the measurements and the positions of building components may be determined.

STANDARD MODULAR COMPONENT

A building component of standardized or specified dimensions which, when used with its joint, fits the standard modular space grid.

STANDARD MODULAR DETAIL

A detailed drawing showing location, measurements, and dimensions of a particular component, or combination of several components, in relation to the standard modular grid.

Note: It is usually drawn at a scale not smaller than ¾" = 1'.

STANDARD MODULAR DIMENSION

(a) A dimension which used once or repeatedly is a multiple of the standard module of 4 inches. (b) The sum of a manufacture dimension and a joint.

STANDARD MODULAR-DIMENSION LINES

(a) Lines which measure the distance between grid lines. (b) Lines measuring distance from grid line to surface, or center line, of a component.

STANDARD MODULAR DRAWING

(a) A drawing showing modular details. (b) A drawing relating by unit measurement (feet, inches) the reference grid lines used in standard modular details to each other. (c) A drawing using standard modular-dimension lines.

STANDARD MODULAR GRID

A reference grid in the standard modular reference system of 4 inches.

STANDARD MODULAR SPACE GRID

A reference space grid with planes spaced at the standard module of 4 inches.

STANDARD MODULE

A module with the dimension of 4 inches.

STRUCTURAL PLANNING GRID

A planning grid on which positions of basic load-bearing structures in the plan of a building are determined.

SUBMODULAR SIZE

A size which is a simple fraction of the basic module.

SYSTEMS OF BUILDING

Simultaneous use of selected building components to form a building (particularly by industrial means).

TOLERANCE

The difference between an actual dimension and the corresponding manufacture dimension. This difference may be positive, negative, or zero.

UPPER DEVIATION

The difference between an upper limit (measurement) and the corresponding nominal measurement. This difference may be positive, negative, or zero.

BIBLIOGRAPHY

Building Products Register, AIA. All dimensional building materials and products identified as to modular characteristics in column #9e. American Institute of Architects, Washington, D. C. 1962, 2nd edition.

Code for Modular Coordination in Building, A-31-1759. Canadian Standards Association.

Current Status of Modular Coordination. Summary of Research Correlation Conference conducted by the Building Research Institute. Includes a review of modular standards, industry efforts, status of adoption, availability of modular products and educational activities incorporating modular coordination. Building Research Institute, National Academy of Sciences-National Research Council, Washington, D. C. 1960.

Development of Standard and Correlated Dimensions of Material-Components in School Construction. Cooperative Research Project No. SAN. 7153, Texas Education Agency, Austin, Texas, and Southwest Research Institute, San Antonio, Texas. 1960.

European Productivity. Articles on building, information on modular coordination and productivity, prefabrication aspects, problems of productivity in Europe. European Productivity Agency, Washington, D. C. March-April, 1957.

Modular Coordination in Building. Summary and analysis of modular work in eleven European countries. European Productivity Agency, Washington, D. C. August, 1956.

Modular Coordination Cuts Design and Building Costs. Stanley R. Kent. Technical Paper 58, National Research Council of Canada, Ottawa, Canada.

Modular Coordination in Practice. Four speeches for architects, contractors, and manufacturers. Technical Paper 79, National Research Council of Canada, Ottawa, Canada.

Modular Dimensioning Practices. Edited papers of one-day modular-dimensioning symposium. Structural Clay Products Institute, Washington, D. C. March, 1959.

Modular Drafting Manual. A guide to preparation of modular working drawings. Stanley R. Kent. Introductory guide in preparing first sets of modular-dimensioned working drawings. NRC No. 6344, National Research Council of Canada, Ottawa, Canada. 1961.

Modular Measure in Residential Construction. Illustration of the modular principles and the drafting techniques as applied to custom, manufactured, and speculative housing. Technical Bulletin 87, Producers' Council, Inc., Washington, D. C. March, 1959.

Modular Quarterly. Continuing reference to current international standards activities, size-range recommendations, and technical considerations of modular planning and production. Modular Society, Ltd., London, England.

MBSA Reports. Technical information on new modular products, news of standards activities, and reprints of recent technical articles on modular practices. Modular Building Standards Association, Washington, D. C.

Modular Slide Series. Nineteen 2 x 2 colored slides prepared for group introduction to modular principles and drafting practices. Syracuse University Audio-Visual Center, Syracuse, New York.

Modular Slide Series Brochure. Twelve-page pamphlet incorporating the illustrations included in the modular slide series, prepared for individual student study following such presentations. Modular Building Standards Association, Washington, D. C.

Reference Working Drawings. Each set contains eight selected sheets from the working drawings of modular-dimensioned projects. Modular Building Standards Association, Washington, D. C.

The current position of modular practice as a design and coordination system with increasing international importance and recognition has developed from the initial work of an American industrialist, Albert Farwell Bemis. As early as 1921, Bemis had started research into the dimensional coordination of building materials and equipment in an effort to improve the existing inefficient methods of the assembly of unrelated materials. Between 1921 and 1936 he developed a basis for dimensional coordination which he called "The Cubical Modular Method." In 1936, in *Rational Design*, the third volume of a three-volume study entitled *The Evolving House*, Bemis sought to apply his knowledge of industrial production techniques to the elimination of inefficiency, waste, and high cost in building construction. He stated that 4 inches provided the largest dimensional increment for minimizing problems in connection with stocking and distributing building products while satisfying the designer's need for flexibility to meet specific requirements, both practical and aesthetic.

After Bemis' death in 1936, his family established the Modular Service Association to cooperate with industry on modular work. Bemis' ideas had struck a responsive chord in the building industry, and in 1938 the American Standards Association, with the aid of the Modular Service Association, conducted a conference of representatives of the building industry to discuss modular coordination. As a result of the favorable recommendations of the participants in the conference, the ASA, in July, 1939, authorized Project A62, with the following scope:

1. The development of a basis for coordinating dimensions of building materials and equipment.

2. The correlation of building plans and details with such dimensions.

3. Recommendations of sizes and dimensions as standards suitable for dimensional correlation.

Project A62 was sponsored by The American Institute of Architects and the Producers' Council, Inc. To carry out the objectives of the project, ASA Sectional Committee A62, composed of almost sixty members representing the construction industry and related fields (architects, engineers, manufacturers, contractors, consumer groups, and government agencies), was organized.

Between 1939 and 1946 the A62 Committee made considerable progress in standards development which led to the adoption of American standards for several types of building materials. An important step was taken in 1945, when the ASA formally approved the 4-inch module as an American standard unit suitable for dimensional coordination. Shortly afterward, in 1946, the Modular

APPENDIX A

BACKGROUND OF MODULAR PRACTICE

Service Association published the first major reference handbook indicating methods of applying modular coordination, *A62 Guide for Modular Coordination.*

In 1948 the Modular Service Association was disbanded, and in 1949 the AIA established an Office of Modular Coordination to act as the focal point for modular activities. A year later the National Association of Home Builders joined the AIA and the Producers' Council as a sponsor of the A62 Committee activities. The Associated General Contractors became the fourth sponsor in 1956.

The Modular Building Standards Association was incorporated in 1957 with the same sponsoring groups as the A62 Committee to carry on the study and promotion of modular practice. It became operational in 1958, with the aims of developing modular standards and preparing educational materials for instruction in modular practice. The MBSA proposed that a guide to modular practices be developed and published to provide assistance in modular procedures to offices and schools. In response to this proposal, the Educational Facilities Laboratories, Inc., provided a grant to the Building Research Advisory Board of the National Academy of Sciences, who contracted with MBSA for the preparation of *Modular Practice.* The Educational Facilities Laboratories is a nonprofit organization established by the Ford Foundation in 1958 to help American schools and colleges with their physical problems by the encouragement of research and experimentation and the dissemination of knowledge regarding educational facilities. The recognition by EFL of the influence which modular practice could have in improving the design and construction of school buildings was a significant step toward modular acceptance in the United States.

Since the publication of Bemis' book, the growth of understanding, acceptance, and use of the principles of modular practice has been slow but steady in the United States. In Europe, the decade of the 1950's was a period of increasing modular awareness with a strong positive approach contributed by the European Productivity Agency of the Organization for European Economic Cooperation. In 1953 and 1954 the EPA started a modular study project in which eleven European nations were to participate. These were Austria, Belgium, Denmark, France, Germany, Greece, Italy, the Netherlands, Norway, Sweden, and the United Kingdom. Canada and the United States, and later Iceland, Turkey, and Yugoslavia, joined the EPA project as observers.

The EPA project, known as Project 174, had as its first phase the collection of information and the shaping of principles and theory. Phase 1 was completed in 1956 with the publication of *Modular Coordination in Building,* a report which dealt with technical aspects of modular theory as applied to design, manufacture, and building. In the Introduction to the Report, industrialization of building is pictured as rapidly changing the nature of building activity in all European countries. A quotation from the Introduction shows the similarity of the European and American approaches:

This is the fundamental problem associated with the industrialization of building: to increase the variety in the types and assembly of components on the site while maintaining a limited range of dimensions for production in the factory.

Modular coordination is the key to the industrialization of building. It is the method by which the dimensions of building parts are coordinated to secure flexibility in use combined with ease of production. It enables a given part to be located in a number of alternative positions, either in the same building or in different buildings, even though that part may be made to one size in one factory. It is to the advantage of all engaged in the industry: architect, manufacturer, and builder.

The second phase of Project 174 was carried out between 1956 and 1960. It involved amplification of the modular theory developed in the first phase by means of further theoretical research and discussion and by constructing trial buildings in the participating countries to clarify the techniques involved in the application of the theory. A final report is being prepared with the title *Coordination of Sizes in Building,* in which the results of the practical planning and construction work are to be evaluated. Continuing work in modular development is to be conducted by the International Standards Organization.

There is no significant difference between modular practice in Europe and in the United States and Canada. In the majority of the European countries, where the metric system is prevalent, a module of 10 centimeters has been adopted, as recommended by the European Productivity Agency. This is very close to the 4-inch module generally used in foot-inch countries and causes no appreciable difference in theory, goals, or application.

Modular practice stands now between a period of study and development and a period of widespread acceptance and application. Research into modular techniques, production of modular materials, and adoption of modular practice by architectural offices will all be parts of the expansion process which will see significant gains in the realization of the benefits of modular practice.

Canadian Building Digest 8, Division of Building Research, National Research Council of Canada, August, 1960, by S. R. Kent.

Modular coordination is the term given to a new procedure for integrating the size of building components so that their assembly may be simplified. It is the first change in measuring for the building industry since the inch and foot were established in uniform lengths by international agreement and became common units of measurement.

For an industry to devise a new unit of measure is not unusual. Many years ago, land sub-dividers found the inch and foot too small for convenience or accuracy and developed the rod, the chain, and the mile as multiples of the smaller units. Similarly the building industry is now finding the inch and its fractions too small for common use and requires a new unit in order to coordinate conveniently the many dimensional parts of a building with accuracy.

The new unit is called the module. Its length is 4 inches, or 10 centimeters in the metric system, as established by standards institutions in Canada, United States, United Kingdom,° Norway, Sweden, Denmark, Russia, Poland, Belgium, France, Italy, Netherlands, Brazil, and Germany.†

THE BUILDING PROCESS

Traditionally, building components have been made on the site from local materials hewn by hand to fit their required position in the structure. Materials were those which could be worked with hand tools into sizes that could be placed into the structure by a craftsman using only the crudest of machinery. Through his skill and ingenuity components were fitted together and secured in place to form walls, floors, and roofs; within the spaces thus created, furnishings and mechanical equipment were put into place.

With the Industrial Revolution came machines to reduce much of the handiwork in building and improved transportation to facilitate trade and provide a variety of materials. Manufacturers and suppliers of building materials joined the contractor in assuming responsibility for the erection of buildings, while the architect, formerly the "master builder," concentrated on planning, designing, and coordinating the building process.

Wherever possible, changes are required to simplify building. To build is still to add one component to another. If components were of soft material like plasticine, they could easily be cut and changed in shape and fitted together by easy manipulation. But this is not the case. Modern building materials are durable and hard. Some may be hand sawn with metal saws; others require specialized equipment. Glass block, double insulating glass, porcelain-glazed sheet metal, metal windows, and mechanical equipment cannot be changed at all in shape after initial manufacture. To combine modern building materials under these restrictive conditions requires newer techniques than those of the traditional craftsman.

At the present time, building components are assem-

° Yet to be published.

† For interior work of a building only.

APPENDIX B

MODULAR COORDINATION

bled either with or without careful pre-planning. In neither method are standard, machine-made component units used exclusively. Without assembly planning, the traditional cut-and-fit procedure takes dominant machine-made components, such as windows and doors, which cannot easily be reshaped on the building site, and adds to them others, such as brick or wood siding, which can be cut. This method is common in light construction where the variety of components is small and those materials cut and wasted are relatively inexpensive.

In assembly planning, drawings are made of the whole building in plan, elevation and section, followed by detail drawings of the component parts, according to manufacturers' catalogue information on size and shape. In spite of the wide range of sizes offered by manufacturers, it is not possible to obtain many components which can be integrated easily because there is no over-all pattern relating the dimensions. Thus dominant components, perhaps those most frequently occurring in the building or the most expensive to obtain in special sizes, are selected from the catalogue; all other components are then established in size on the drawings so that they can be manufactured as required. This planning procedure is essential for large projects because of the necessity of fitting together not only the components for the structure but also the heating and ventilating, plumbing, electrical, and other mechanical equipment. It does result in less cutting and reshaping on the site, but much time is spent in selecting from the catalogues those few components which do coordinate in size and in preparing precision drawings for the shop manufacture of the special sizes.

In the first method, time and material are wasted in cutting and fitting on the site, where the waste is readily seen; in the second method, time is wasted in offices and in the efficient operation of machines making wide ranges and special sizes of components. Both building methods are handicapped by the waste resulting from the uncoordinated dimensions of the components.

A COORDINATING DIMENSION FOR ALL COMPONENTS

In selecting a dimension which can be used to coordinate the sizes of all components likely to be used in every type of building, attempts have been made to determine the dimension common to the majority. Unfortunately, because of the vast number of existing sizes, it has not been easy to find a common denominator. The dimension must be small enough to permit sufficient variation in total sizes; if 1 foot is selected, then doors would be 2, 3, or 4 feet and walls 1 or 2 feet thick. These excessive totals or multiples of the coordinating dimension would be wasteful of material and make economical planning impossible. On the other hand, if the dimension is too small, such as 1 inch, there is the possibility of as great a variety of sizes for the machine to make as now exists.

From the results of studies in different parts of the world, the dimension of 4 inches, and in countries using the metric system 10 centimeters, has been found most satisfactory. Thus a coordinating unit of measurement has been accepted which may be repeated in the sizes of all building components; the name for this unit is the standard building *Module*.

The word module comes from the Latin *modulus*, meaning measure. Since module does not denote a size in terms of a common unit of measurement, its use when applied to coordination in building has led to much confusion. As previously shown, the basis for coordination must be an agreed denominator for the sizes of building components in inches or centimeters. Manufacturers may advertise "modular" desks, cabinets, and other fitments, which by themselves fit together because of some repeated measurement, as do children's blocks or the pieces in the game of dominoes, but the products do not bear any dimensional relationship to the other components in a building.

In establishing the building module as 4 inches, the possibility of dimensions other than simple multiples is not eliminated, because either custom or manufacturing and assembly methods may require that a component have a dimension smaller than the module in one or more dimensions. For these components to be useful modular size, two or more components are joined together to total a dimension which is a multiple of 4 inches. The most common example of this type of component is the clay brick. Owing to the manufacturing problems of firing large volumes of clay to a uniform dimension in the kiln, the height of the brick is kept less than 4 inches. As the next higher modular dimension is eight, bricks are sized so that three bricks, with their joints, will equal 8 inches, the modular height of each brick being 2⅔ inches.

MODULAR COMPONENTS

Having once set the standard building module, a uniform procedure may be laid down for any manufacturer to follow in order that the different components, when added together in the building, will total modular dimensions. The procedure recognizes three facts: (1) that between all components there is a space or joint, (2) that the joint may vary from the "best" size to a practicable maximum or minimum, and (3) that the components may vary from the manufacturers' "intended" size to a practicable oversize or undersize as a result of uncontrollable or unpredictable physical changes in the material during manufacture, expansion or contraction due to temperature or humidity, or lack of precision manufacturing machinery.

In standards of the Canadian Standards Association, the Canadian Government Specifications Board, and those of trade associations, manufacturers and builders have already agreed on reasonable deviations from the intended or "manufacture" size which are in keeping with good building practice and quality manufacturing; and through job experience manufacturers and builders know the desirable size and acceptable maximum and minimum sizes of the joints required by the various components for sound construction. Therefore, the procedure simply requires that the sum of each component and its joint never be greater than a multiple of 4 inches, even when the component varies to its maximum manufactured oversize limit and the joint is at its minimum acceptable size; nor less than a multiple of 4 inches, when the component varies to its minimum manufactured undersize limit and the joint is at its maximum acceptable size.

MODULAR RANGE OF COMPONENTS

It is an economic necessity for a manufacturer to produce components only in a limited range of sizes, being certain at the same time that they will readily fit other building components. Yet with this restriction a sufficient number of sizes must be provided for adequate flexibility in the arrangement of components for variation in building design. Such a limited coordinating range is possible where manufacturers agree to select sizes from a framework of modular dimensions.

For some components, all their modular dimensions will be an even multiple of 4 inches (a concrete block 8 by 8 by 16 inches), while in others only two may be modular and the third non-modular (glass thickness, a non-additive dimension). In establishing a range, not every multiple of 4 inches should be selected for a component. Instead numbers such as 4, 8, 12, and 16 at the lower end of the order of multiples are preferred, since greater flexibility can be achieved with additive combinations of the smaller numbers.

The range will be further reduced by elimination of dimensions which create components of aesthetically disturbing proportions, such as those which are almost square, 40 by 44 inches, or too long and narrow for manufacturing or installation practicality; by components having to "fill in" between dimensions set by building codes; or by anthropometrical dimensions, such as door, desk, and ceiling heights. For example, in Sweden door components are two modular heights, 6 feet 8 inches and 7 feet, and four widths, 2 feet 4 inches, 2 feet 8 inches, 3 feet 0 inch, and 3 feet 4 inches.

MODULAR DIMENSIONS ON WORKING DRAWINGS

Throughout the building process, dimensions of components must be transmitted between architect, contractor, manufacturer, and craftsman. To avoid confusion and error, these instructions should be simple and clear. Mistakes often result when dimensions are difficult to read because there are too many fractional numbers crowded on a small drawing, or they are awkward to enunciate, record, add, and subtract. Such mistakes are particularly costly when factory-made components which cannot be corrected on the job site are used.

The transmittance of modular dimensions is clear and simple, either by feet and inches in 4-inch multiples (e.g., 2 feet 8 inches by 9 feet 4 inches) or by a certain number of the 4-inch modules (e.g., 8M by 28M). These non-fractional numbers may be clearly shown on assembly drawings when the scale of the drawing is as small as ⅛ or 1/16 inch to the foot. Such small-scale drawings are quicker to draw, as unessential, fine detail is eliminated, and complete plans of large floor areas may be shown on one convenient-size sheet of paper, i.e., at 1/16 inch to the foot a floor 480 by 640 feet within 30 by 40 inches. But whether modular assembly drawings are made at the smaller scales or at ¼ inch to the foot, modular dimensions assist building contractors to reduce errors in taking off quantities and in site assembly.

To use modular dimensions properly, however, requires a complete understanding of what they really are. They are not usually measured from the surface of components, as in nonmodular drawings, but from grid lines which control the sizes of components as the basis for coordination. Therefore, there must be a description of the distance or offset between the surface of the component and the grid line to which the dimension is given. For most components this is one-half the established assembly joint of the component. This may be done in the large-scale drawing, 1½ inches to the foot or 3 inches to the foot, that is commonly prepared for contract work, or in accepted industrial modular standards. Ultimately, most common components and their assembly joints will be described in the latter manner. as is already being achieved in Scandinavian countries, so that architects, manufacturers, and all tradesmen will become familiar with them and their repetition on working drawings will be unnecessary.

In small-scale assembly drawings, where it is impossible to show both the grid line and the actual surface of the component, as the two may be less than a pencil line's width apart, there should be clarification of the fact that the given dimension is to a grid line, which is preferable as previously shown, or to an off-grid point. This may be done by establishing the following drawing convention. "Dimensions given to a grid line: have the dimension line terminated with an arrowhead. Dimension given to an actual surface or point not on a grid line: have the dimension line terminated with a dot."

Continual developments in technology and mechanization are providing the building industry with larger and larger building components, together with methods of putting them in place on the site. Factory-made components such as curtain-wall panels, office partition walls, precast concrete stairs, precast concrete structural floor panels, and steel framing members can be used to the best advantage by planning for them during the early stages of the design work with the aid of a "planning grid." This planning grid is determined by the modular size of the components being used, so that there is assurance that whole components will fit into place without alterations.

ASSEMBLY OF MODULAR COMPONENTS

Manufacturing components in modular sizes and planning their assembly on paper are of limited value unless a similar degree of precision can be achieved in field assembly. A procedure for the accurate location of components must be introduced to many trades which at present are unaccustomed to factory-like precision work. Fortunately this can be done very easily by the reference grid system.

When a building is laid out on the site, a reference grid datum point is established; from this point horizontal and vertical grid lines are measured, radiating at 4-inch intervals. Only the position of the principal grid lines shown in the assembly drawing need be measured off, as it is from these that the actual position of a component is obtained by applying a dimension which is customary for the particular component in modular construction, or which is shown on the detail working drawing.

As an aid in finding the position of grid lines, it may be convenient to have a tape, and for laying modular masonry units a story-pole, marked off in 4-inch intervals. By constantly relating components to this grid position, there is no chance of their gradually creeping out of place and causing an error in an over-all measurement. This checking permits a deviation in the size of a component to be absorbed in its own joint, rather than have them accumulate.

CONCLUSION

The foregoing has been a summary of what is meant by the term "modular coordination" with some indication as to how this development in measurement can be applied in manufacturing, in building design, and on the construction job. The constructive results of its application will steadily increase as its use extends. The Division of Building Research is preparing publications showing how the modular system can be applied primarily in design work. Further information will be gladly provided to those wishing to see how the system can be applied to their own work.

Cooperative Research Project No. SAN. 7153, Texas Education Agency, Austin, Texas, and Southwest Research Institute, San Antonio, Texas, 1960.

NOTE: *The material in Appendix C is based on research performed pursuant to a contract with the United States Office of Education, Department of Health, Education, and Welfare, and presented in a full report, "Development of Standard and Correlated Dimensions of Material-Components in School Construction," published by the Texas Education Agency, Austin, Texas, July, 1960. The basic material for Appendix C was prepared by Norman I. Turner, Research Architect, Southwest Research Institute.*

INTRODUCTION

Modular coordination for an architectural program is the achievement of dimensional order through the use of a system or technique which relates all items, dimensional in nature, by utilizing a linkage system created from basic roots or modules. A system for modular coordination, at each stage of the architectural process, must furnish the means of establishing a dimensional reference by which the sizes of spaces and areas resulting from the building design, as well as the sizes of material products, may be dimensionally related and made compatible.

Such a system makes possible a high degree of efficiency in construction coordination. It does not, however, guarantee that such efficiency is attained unconditionally throughout all areas of application. A particular building product or construction system can be only as dimensionally efficient as its range of sizes allows within its own material system. In cases where these material systems are utilized, the importance of the over-all system for design and construction is that it provides for dimensional compatibility between the several material systems.

DESCRIPTION

The system presented here is used for correlating dimensions of building spaces, building elements, and materials, and as an aid to the coordination of construction details. Various techniques within the system are available and may be applied where desirable. These are called "segments" of the system. To support the segments, particular tools or aids are available which, when utilized with the segments, provide for design, construction, and fabrication on a coordinated modular basis. The fundamental roots upon which both the segments and the tools or aids are based are 3, 4, and 5. When a dimensional unit is assigned to these roots, such as the inch (English system of units), they

APPENDIX C

A SYSTEM FOR MODULAR COORDINATION

become the basic modules of the system (3, 4, and 5 inches). The modules may be used singly or in combination. Their selection is at the discretion of those employing these techniques.

System segments. The first segment, or principal technique, of the system is the establishment of principal planes of reference, as shown in Figure C-1. These planes, positioned by the architect or designer, are placed at precise locations dictated by the particular design. The location of the planes is influenced by the specific considerations, such as the main configuration of the design, the construction system, the materials, the structure, and the elevations. Wherever it seems best to establish the base for dimensional reference, these planes, which show as lines in plan, section, and elevation, are located. They form the main reference lines and are identified by letters or numerals in bold triangles. The distance between these principal reference planes is determined precisely by the modular sequence of divisions within or between two or more planes. This may be set by the designer according to the modules selected for the particular design.

The second segment, modulation, shown in Figure C-2, is the means by which a linear dimension is represented by a combination or grouping of basic modules. Such groupings may be repetitive modules producing a multiple sequence or a combination of two or three modules producing an additive sequence. This dimensional subdivision by modulation produces a grid pattern representative of the particular module sequences selected. These grids are imaginary but may appear on the drawings wherever required as an aid to dimensional correlation. The two methods of modulation will be described under the tools and aids section.

The third segment of the system is modular correlation. This is accomplished first by ensuring that the various grid patterns resulting from modulation form an uninterrupted sequence, that each initial grid line of a pattern sequence coincides with the last grid line of the previous pattern, and that all grid patterns mesh or are coincident with the principal planes of reference, the reference frame. In addition, correlation is the technique by which the various components, materials, and building elements may be positioned, ensuring over-all dimen-

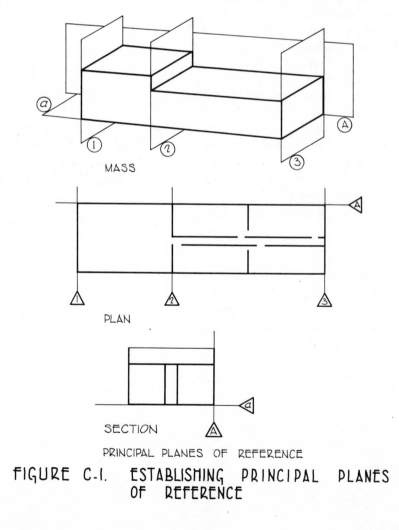

MASS

PLAN

SECTION

PRINCIPAL PLANES OF REFERENCE

FIGURE C-1. ESTABLISHING PRINCIPAL PLANES OF REFERENCE

sional compatibility, and at the same time suiting the design and modulation sequences selected by the architect.

Coordination, the fourth and final segment, shown in Figure C-3, is that portion of the system process where final organization of the construction is achieved dimensionally within the grid patterns and planes of elements, at the juncture of the material elements. It is here that the coordination relationships are made final by determining the dimensions of the details between the particular construction systems and the material products. The actual construction details are determined not by the system, but by the designer. The coordination effort is the detailing part of design.

System tools and aids. These tools are specific devices and methods provided to aid those utilizing the various segments of the system. The first of these, and a basic tool of modular coordination, is the number pattern.

The number pattern, shown in Figure C-4, is a general numerical reference which expresses the relation of all numbers based on the roots or coefficients 3, 4, and 5. It is an empirical table which, when assigned a unit of measure, will provide groups and sequences of dimensions in any magnitude of range with a common linkage of 3, 4, 5, or a combination of these. During the application of the segments, certain controlling dimensions, specifically appropriate for the particular design under study, will be apparent. Since the numbers representing these dimensions must be related, reference is made to the number pattern for the appropriate module relationship which will satisfy the conditions of the design solution. By reference to the pattern, appropriate number combinations and pattern ranges are selected to support the specific conditions of the design. As the range of numbers increases, and as the complexity of design or coordination becomes more involved, the order of numerical sequences increases. Thus, a more definitive reference is provided as an auxiliary and companion tool, the number-combination table.

Number-combination tables, as seen in Figure C-5, disclose the combinations and sequence of basic roots or modules which make up any number in the number pattern. These tables are arranged for each number and give all the variations of 3, 4,

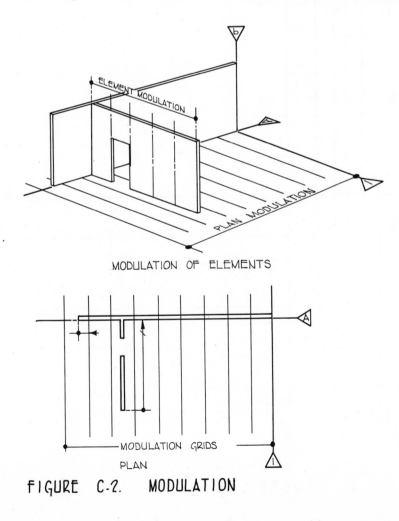

MODULATION OF ELEMENTS

MODULATION GRIDS

PLAN

FIGURE C-2.   MODULATION

and 5, as additives and as multiples comprising the particular number. These numerical combinations are employed to set the related dimensional units of design and construction and may be expressed graphically as representative grid patterns.

The grid patterns are also correlation aids within the system and result from the two methods of modulation, which in turn utilize the number pattern and companion combination tables. These grids serve as a means for dimensional order and act as a key to a controlled network based on the particular module pattern selected for a specific design.

The two methods of modulation are termed "rigid modulation" and "combination modulation." Rigid modulation employs a single root or module, either 3, 4, or 5. This produces a repetitive multiple grid pattern whose grid-line spacing has a fixed order of magnitude in either direction. Thus, a repeated square or rectangular grid is the result. Combina-

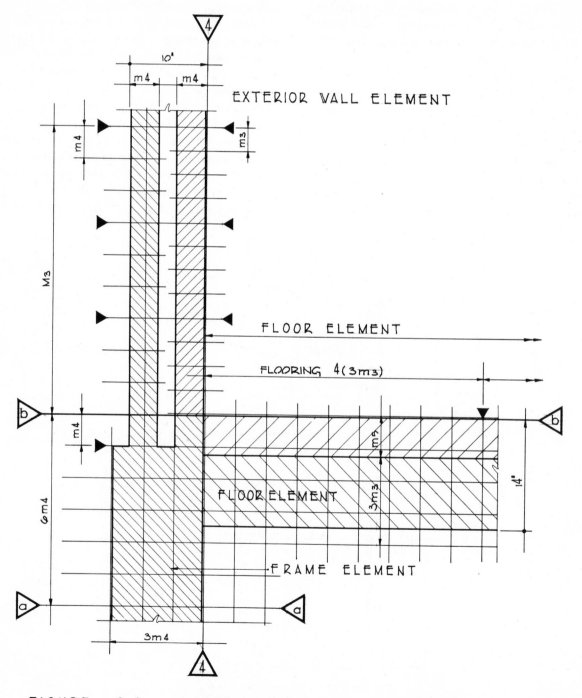

FIGURE C-3.   COORDINATION   OF   ELEMENTS

NUMBER RELATIONS

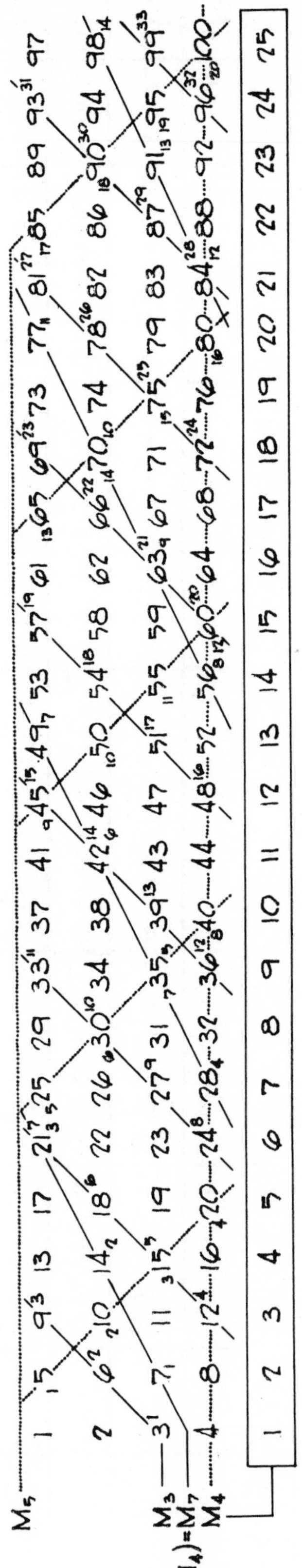

SwRI NUMBER PATTERN

FIGURE C-4.   THE NUMBER PATTERN

64

D*	3	4	5
13	0	1	12
14	0	6	8
	1	4	9
	2	2	10
	3	0	11
15	0	11	4
	1	9	5
	2	7	6
	3	5	7
	4	3	8
	5	1	9
16	0	16	0
	1	14	1
	2	12	2
	3	10	3
	4	8	4
	5	6	5
	6	4	6
	7	2	7
	8	0	8
17	4	13	0
	5	11	1
	6	9	2
	7	7	3
	8	5	4
	9	3	5
	10	1	6
18	8	10	0
	9	8	1
	10	6	2
	11	4	3
	12	2	4
	13	0	5
19	12	7	0
	13	5	1
	14	3	2
	15	1	3
20	16	4	0
	17	2	1
	18	0	2
21	20	1	0

* DIVISIONS

65

D	3	4	5
13	0	0	13
14	0	5	9
	1	3	10
	2	1	11
15	0	10	5
	1	8	6
	2	6	7
	3	4	8
	4	2	9
	5	0	10
16	0	15	1
	1	13	2
	2	11	3
	3	9	4
	4	7	5
	5	5	6
	6	3	7
	7	1	8
17	3	14	0
	4	12	1
	5	10	2
	6	8	3
	7	6	4
	8	4	5
	9	2	6
	10	0	7
18	7	11	0
	8	9	1
	9	7	2
	10	5	3
	11	3	4
	12	1	5
19	11	8	0
	12	6	1
	13	4	2
	14	2	3
	15	0	4
20	15	5	0
	16	3	1
	17	1	2
21	19	2	0
	20	0	1

66

D	3	4	5
14	0	4	10
	1	2	11
	2	0	12
15	0	9	6
	1	7	7
	2	5	8
	3	3	9
	4	1	10
16	0	14	2
	1	12	3
	2	10	4
	3	8	5
	4	6	6
	5	4	7
	6	2	8
	7	0	9
17	2	15	0
	3	13	1
	4	11	2
	5	9	3
	6	7	4
	7	5	5
	8	3	6
	9	1	7
18	6	12	0
	7	10	1
	8	8	2
	9	6	3
	10	4	4
	11	2	5
	12	0	6
19	10	9	0
	11	7	1
	12	5	2
	13	3	3
	14	1	4
20	14	6	0
	15	4	1
	16	2	2
	17	0	3
21	18	3	0
	19	1	1
22	22	0	0

FIGURE C-5.   NUMBER COMBINATION TABLES

tion modulation employs two or more modules, 3 and 4, 3 and 5, or 4 and 5, in one or both directions. This produces a grid pattern which expresses an additive sequence, and the square or rectangular pattern varies dependent upon the specific sequences selected. Thus, the graphic expression of this grid pattern is not necessarily regular or repetitive. These concepts are shown in Figure C-6.

Additional aids are graphic symbols, shown in Figure C-7, used on drawings as the representation of particular operations within the system. The principal reference planes, which show as lines on the drawings, are identified at their termination with bold triangles. These lines are repeated on the various drawings to key the details to respective plans, elevations, or sections. Dimension lines are terminated with specific symbols. Where dimensions terminate on grid lines, arrowheads are used. Dots are used where dimensions do not terminate on grid lines. Also, dimensioning

which shows the extent of an element or series of components will indicate by a mark on this line whether the components or subelements comprise standard modular material sizes.

USE OF THE SYSTEM

Architect, designer, engineer. The system, as employed by the architect, is used to reference and relate dimensionally building spaces, building elements, and materials and to aid in the coordination of construction details. The first step is the establishment of the principal planes of reference which form the reference frame. This frame serves as the datum or skeleton for the total dimensional process involved in planning, design, and the production of construction drawings. The engineers then use these principal frames as their data of dimensional reference.

The architect or designer employs the technique

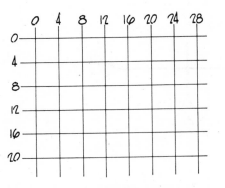

GRID LINE SPACING EQUAL
IN BOTH DIRECTIONS.

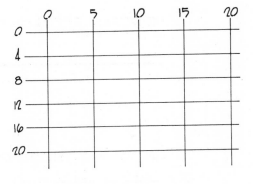

GRID LINE SPACING EQUAL IN
EACH OF TWO DIRECTIONS.

GRIDS REPRESENTING RIGID MODULATION

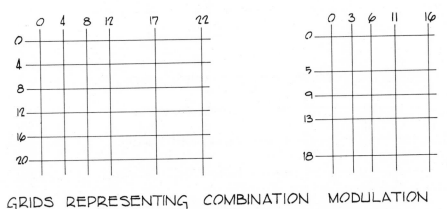

GRIDS REPRESENTING COMBINATION MODULATION

FIGURE C-6.   RIGID AND COMBINATION MODULATION

of modulation to relate in an orderly fashion the dimensional aspects of the entire building complex. In this way a pattern is formed for the positioning and relating of components within elements and in turn for referencing these parts, including elements, to the reference frames.

With the use of this technique, the architect and engineer correlate dimensionally elements to elements, material systems to material systems, and component-product units to component units. By correlation the various increments of assemblies are dimensionally related and fixed within the reference lines of the system. The final effort, coordination, is attained by the designer. Up to this stage, the elements and construction systems have been related dimensionally by the employment of the linkage medium of modulation. Coordination, however, requires the detailed junction of the building

material parts and elements one to another. By specific solution these details are created by the designer to allow the parts to be assembled in a manner which is acceptable designwise and is feasible constructionwise.

Producer-fabricator. The material fabricator is concerned with the efficient use of bulk stock, the production of stock component parts, and subassemblies. He is concerned further with the development of a range of sizes of particular products so that they may be used efficiently with those of other manufacturers and will fill the size preferences desired by the industry. The producer utilizes the number-pattern and number-combination tables to develop within a material range sizes compatible with those of other component parts. If the product is a complex assembly of parts comprising a construction system, modulation will create a

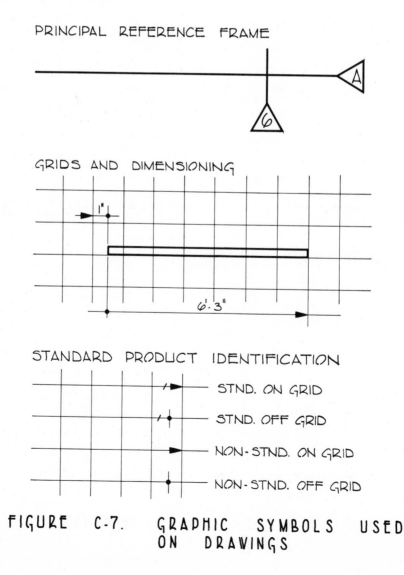

TOOLS AND AIDS

PRINCIPAL REFERENCE FRAME

GRIDS AND DIMENSIONING

STANDARD PRODUCT IDENTIFICATION

STND. ON GRID

STND. OFF GRID

NON-STND. ON GRID

NON-STND. OFF GRID

FIGURE   C-7.   GRAPHIC SYMBOLS USED
ON DRAWINGS

dimensional pattern for the sizing and assembly of these parts into an acceptable range of element sizes. It will assure that such sizing will satisfy the greatest possible demand and range of use without further shop or job-site resizing. The appropriate reference grids defining the element or component sizes may then be used by the architect at the stage where he is modulating the particular building design for which these manufactured items will be supplied.

Contractor. The element of the system used most frequently by construction personnel is the reference frame. The principal frames of reference determined by the architect will serve as a base at the job site for verification of dimensions in accordance with those set by design. Grids resulting from modulation will be used by subcontractors in the dimensioning of shop drawings and as check reference points during the assembly of their materials and components into the building elements.

NOMENCLATURE

Additive composition grid. A (grid) pattern in a single plane consisting of a series of parallel lines in each of two directions but spaced to express a particular scaled relation of selected modular units.

Complex element. A building element comprising a group of materials and/or components which by their nature require different systems of jointure.

Correlation. The act of relating or referencing by dimension either the plane of an element, subelement, or material to the grid line of a grid pattern or the grid line of one pattern to that of another.

Discipline. Control gained by enforcing order; hence, orderly disposition.

Element (building element). Any generic assemblage of building materials and/or components to form an en-closure of space; a more or less complex constituent part of a building having its own functional identity, e.g., walls, floors, roof, partitions.

Grid. A pattern of lines, usually in a single plane, composed of two families of (grid) lines.

Grid line. One of a family of parallel lines in a particular reference grid pattern to which materials or elements may be dimensioned.

Mesh line. The grid line of two families of grid patterns; the common grid line of one pattern or family which is coincident with the grid line of another pattern having a different spacing.

Modular coordination. Achievement of dimensional order with the use of a system or technique which relates items, dimensional in nature, by utilizing a linkage system created from basic roots or modules.

Modulation. A technique applied to an element or area to develop a reference grid pattern whose grid-line spacing is determined by the particular modulation method selected.

Modulation methods. The means of regulating or governing selected increments of measure called "modules" so as to accomplish desirable dimensional relations for modular coordination purposes.

Module. A common unit of measure.

Number pattern. A selected set of numbers particularly composed on one or more planes to express their determined relations.

Range of sizes (material). Integer multiples applied to a basic material dimension to produce limits in a series of actual or possible size variations in building products.

Reference grid pattern. A system comprising two families of parallel lines in one plane usually at right angles to each other, a constant or variable distance apart in each of two directions, used as a dimensional reference for materials and elements.

Rigid multiple grid. A regular (grid) pattern in a single plane consisting of a series of parallel lines at a constant spacing in each of two directions.

Subelement. A group of materials or components comprising one jointure system within a complex element.

Architectural Research Project conducted at the Department of Architecture, College of Environmental Design, University of California, Berkeley, California.

NOTE: *The material in Appendix D is based on research performed by Professor Ezra D. Ehrenkrantz of the University of California. The basic material for Appendix D was prepared by Professor Ehrenkrantz.*

APPENDIX D

THE MODULAR NUMBER PATTERN

Modular coordination is defined here as a keyboard for design which provides flexibility while using standard products. The need for this has been brought about by the development of machine-made, rather than hand-made, products and components. The economics of technological production requires that products be produced to fixed sizes. Since the architect must combine the fixed, available sizes of many products in the solution of a design problem, it is essential that these products relate to one another for efficient, economical construction.

A number of approaches have been made to the problem of relating, or coordinating, building products. Most of them make use of a specific dimension to which the products are designed and manufactured. In some cases this dimension is small, such as 4 inches; in some it is intermediate, such as 1 to 10 feet; and in some it is large, such as 10 to 25 feet. It is essential that any system of modular coordination should work in terms of some such established standard, and at the same time that it should provide an aesthetically neutral keyboard with respect to design. Modular coordination also should be flexible enough to accommodate new technological developments.

A single coordinated system is necessary which will provide sufficient design flexibility with standard components so that architects do not have to call for special ones, and which will restrict the number of component sizes so that industry can standardize efficiently on a fixed number of product sizes and types. This requires that the products of the entire building industry be related to one another dimensionally so that they can be put together in an infinite variety of ways. This coordination must be accomplished with products of different materials, end conditions, and manufacturing methods. As it is virtually impossible to find a meaningful common denominator which will relate to all products, another way must be found to relate the various products to each other.

An obvious way to accomplish this purpose is to develop groups of building components which have flexibility to increments of a very small size, although each product may be relatively large. A group of partition elements might have flexibility

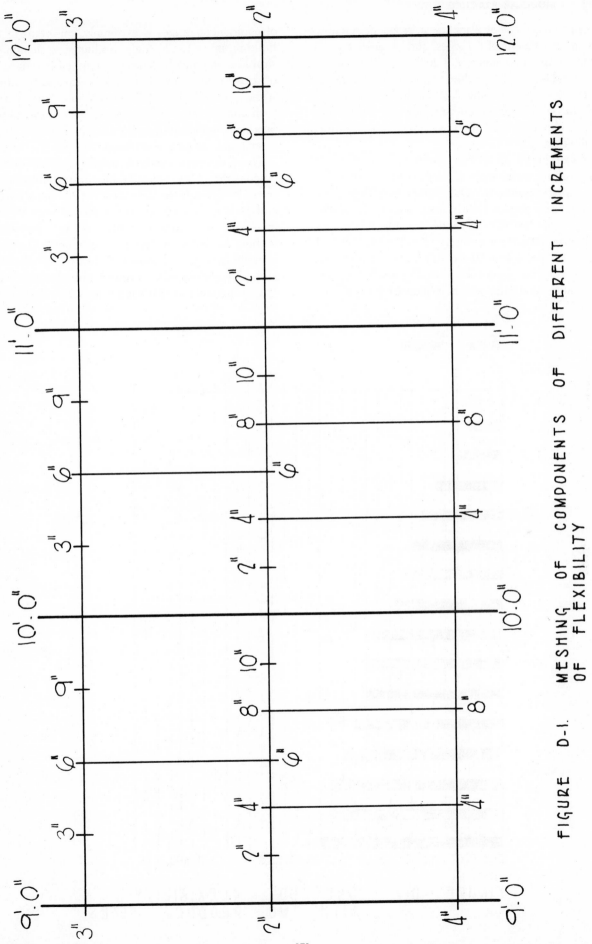

FIGURE D-1. MESHING OF COMPONENTS OF DIFFERENT INCREMENTS
OF FLEXIBILITY

to any increment of 2 inches, a group of windows to any increment of 3 inches, and an acoustic ceiling to any increment of 4 inches. As shown in Figure D-1, these products can be used together and have specific points of meshing, although it would be difficult to combine a single 30-inch partition element, a 45-inch window, and a 24-inch ceiling panel.

Flexibility to small increments may be obtained by working with ranges of product sizes rather than with single products. Only 4-foot flexibility in design can be obtained with one product size of 4′0″, but 1-foot flexibility is made possible if 3′0″ and 4′0″ product sizes are used. (See Figure D-2.) If an additional size of 30 inches is added, 6-inch flexibility may be obtained. (See Figure D-3.) This flexibility of design which is increased by the use

of component ranges is extremely important in the building process. A single product size, though desirable economically, leads to complications in terms of corner conditions, wall thicknesses, and structural sizes. Three or four different product sizes with a variation of only a few inches may provide the necessary compensation for various material thicknesses and jointing conditions.

Three different product ranges are used here to demonstrate how considerable design freedom is possible through the development of these ranges, and how each product group has its own unique increment of flexibility which cannot be altered without basically changing the product. The three product groups are movable partitions, windows, and plywood panels. Present material sizes and shapes are used so that suggestions which are made

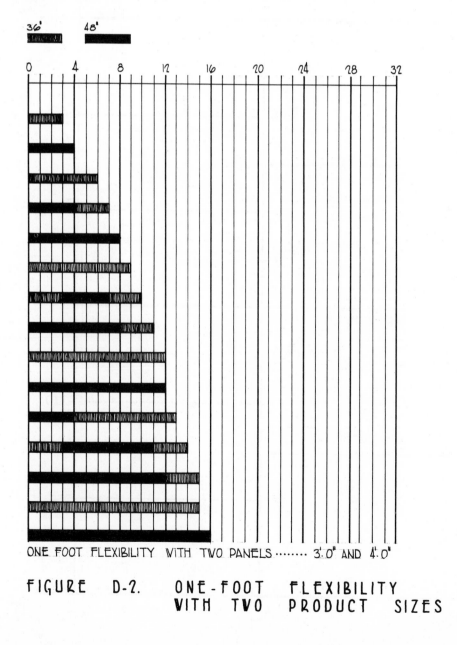

ONE FOOT FLEXIBILITY WITH TWO PANELS ········ 3′0″ AND 4′0″

FIGURE D-2. ONE-FOOT FLEXIBILITY WITH TWO PRODUCT SIZES

will be feasible within current manufacturing processes.

MOVABLE PARTITIONS

An analysis of the sizes of partition elements produced by four major manufacturers showed that the smallest number of sizes produced by one firm was ten and the largest, nineteen. If only eight of those produced were used, flexibility could be obtained to increments of 2 inches. This is done by combining sizes which are multiples of 6 inches with sizes which are multiples of 4 inches. Thus, by the use of the 20-, 30-, 40-, and 42-inch sizes with the foot-multiple sizes of 24, 36, 48, and 60 inches, 2-inch design flexibility is achieved. This is shown in Figure D-4.

Combinations which are shown in Figure D-4 are illustrated at 9′4″ and 9′6″ in Figure D-5 to indicate the considerable choice which is open to the architect. The use of this type of product range requires no change in any industrial process. The only change involved would be the reduction of the number of standard sizes. With the flexibility made possible by the remaining sizes, rooms of any desired dimensions could be obtained without cutting and fitting of the partition elements.

WINDOWS

One of the standard products which is most difficult to coordinate dimensionally with others is the metal window, as the standard sizes of most windows are ⅞ inch larger than a 4-inch multiple. As a result metal windows come in such sizes as 1′8⅞″, 2′0⅞″, 2′8⅞″, and 3′0⅞″. The extra ⅞ inch develops from the fact that the typical mullion may vary from 2⅜ inches to 3⅛ inches, and the maximum mullion size plus ⅞ inch equals the next 4-inch multiple. Two windows plus a 3⅛-inch

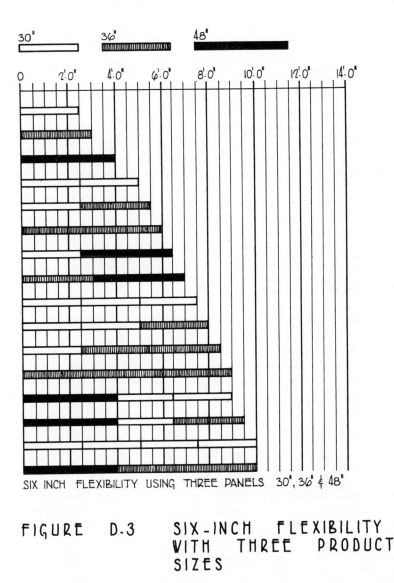

SIX INCH FLEXIBILITY USING THREE PANELS 30″, 36″ & 48″

FIGURE D-3   SIX-INCH FLEXIBILITY WITH THREE PRODUCT SIZES

20	24	30	36	40	42	48	60

5'0"   20 + 20 + 20
        24 + 36
        20 + 40
        30 + 30
        60
                                        5'2"   20 + 42

5'4"   24 + 40
        24 + 20 + 20
                                        5'6"   30 + 36
                                                24 + 42

5'8"   24 + 20 + 24
        48 + 20
                                        5'10"   20 + 30 + 20
                                                30 + 40

6'0"   24 + 24 + 24
        48 + 24
        36 + 36
        42 + 30
                                        6'2"   20 + 24 + 30

6'4"   36 + 20 + 20
        36 + 40
                                        6'6"   36 + 42
                                                30 + 48
                                                24 + 30 + 24

6'8"   20 + 20 + 20 + 20
        20 + 40 + 20
        40 + 40
        36 + 24 + 20
        60 + 20
        20 + 30 + 30
                                        6'10"   42 + 20 + 20
                                                42 + 40

7'0"   24 + 20 + 20 + 20
        24 + 36 + 24
        20 + 40 + 24
        48 + 36
        24 + 60
        42 + 42
        30 + 30 + 24
                                        7'2"   30 + 20 + 36
                                                20 + 42 + 24

7'4"   24 + 20 + 24 + 20
        24 + 40 + 24
        20 + 48 + 20
        48 + 40
                                        7'6"   30 + 30 + 30
                                                30 + 60
                                                48 + 42
                                                24 + 42 + 24
                                                24 + 36 + 30
                                                20 + 20 + 20 + 30
                                                30 + 20 + 40

7'8"   24 + 20 + 24 + 24
        24 + 20 + 48
        36 + 36 + 20
        20 + 30 + 42
                                        7'10"   30 + 40 + 24
                                                24 + 30 + 20 + 20

8'0"   24 + 24 + 24 + 24
        48 + 24 + 24
        48 + 48
        36 + 24 + 36
        20 + 20 + 36 + 20
        20 + 36 + 40
        36 + 60
        30 + 30 + 36
        42 + 24 + 30
                                        8'2"   24 + 24 + 20 + 30
                                                48 + 20 + 30
                                                42 + 20 + 36

8'4"   20 + 20 + 30 + 30
        30 + 30 + 40
        20 + 20 + 20 + 20 + 20
        36 + 24 + 20 + 20
        20 + 20 + 20 + 40
        40 + 20 + 40
        36 + 24 + 40
        60 + 20 + 20
        60 + 40
                                        8'6"   36 + 30 + 36
                                                30 + 24 + 48
                                                24 + 24 + 24 + 30
                                                60 + 42
                                                30 + 42 + 30
                                                36 + 24 + 42
                                                20 + 20 + 20 + 42
                                                20 + 40 + 42

<u>20</u>	<u>24</u>	<u>30</u>	<u>36</u>	<u>40</u>	<u>42</u>	<u>48</u>	<u>60</u>

8'8"
20 + 24 + 30 + 30
42 + 20 + 42
24 + 20 + 20 + 20 + 20
24 + 20 + 24 + 36
24 + 20 + 40 + 20
40 + 24 + 40
60 + 20 + 24
48 + 20 + 36

8'10"
24 + 42 + 20 + 20
24 + 42 + 40
30 + 36 + 20 + 20
30 + 36 + 40

9'0"
42 + 36 + 30
24 + 20 + 20 + 20 + 24
24 + 24 + 24 + 36
48 + 20 + 20 + 20
48 + 24 + 36
60 + 48
36 + 36 + 36
30 + 30 + 48
30 + 30 + 24 + 24
60 + 24 + 24
36 + 42 + 30

9'2"
30 + 40 + 40
30 + 20 + 20 + 40
30 + 20 + 20 + 20 + 20
60 + 30 + 20
24 + 36 + 30 + 20
30 + 30 + 30 + 20
42 + 24 + 24 + 20
42 + 20 + 48

9'4"
30 + 40 + 42
30 + 20 + 20 + 42
24 + 20 + 24 + 20 + 24
48 + 20 + 20 + 24
40 + 24 + 24 + 24
40 + 48 + 24
40 + 36 + 36
20 + 20 + 36 + 36

9'6"
36 + 42 + 36
24 + 42 + 48
60 + 24 + 30
30 + 30 + 24 + 30
36 + 24 + 24 + 30
42 + 24 + 24 + 24
42 + 42 + 30
30 + 20 + 20 + 42

9'8"
36 + 20 + 20 + 20 + 20
36 + 20 + 24 + 36
20 + 40 + 36 + 20
36 + 40 + 40
60 + 20 + 36
48 + 20 + 48
24 + 24 + 48 + 20
24 + 24 + 20 + 24 + 24
20 + 24 + 30 + 42
20 + 30 + 30 + 36

9'10"
24 + 30 + 40 + 24
48 + 30 + 40
24 + 30 + 20 + 20 + 24
42 + 36 + 20 + 20
42 + 36 + 40
20 + 20 + 30 + 48

10'0"
20 + 20 + 20 + 20 + 20 + 20
20 + 20 + 20 + 20 + 40
20 + 20 + 40 + 40
24 + 36 + 20 + 20 + 20
24 + 24 + 24 + 24 + 24
24 + 36 + 24 + 36
24 + 36 + 20 + 40
40 + 40 + 40
60 + 60
60 + 20 + 20 + 20
60 + 36 + 24
60 + 20 + 40
48 + 24 + 48
36 + 48 + 36
48 + 24 + 24 + 24
30 + 30 + 60
30 + 48 + 42
30 + 30 + 30 + 30
20 + 40 + 30 + 30
24 + 24 + 30 + 42

FIGURE D-4.   TWO-INCH FLEXIBILITY WITH EIGHT PRODUCT SIZES

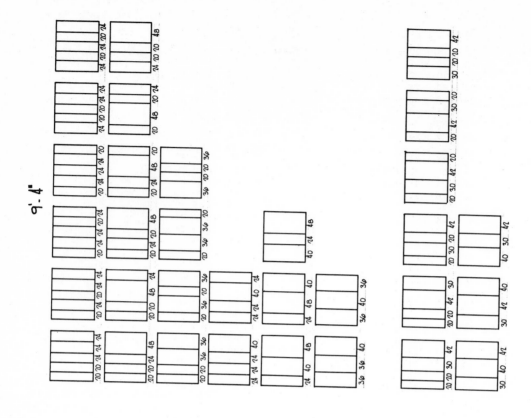

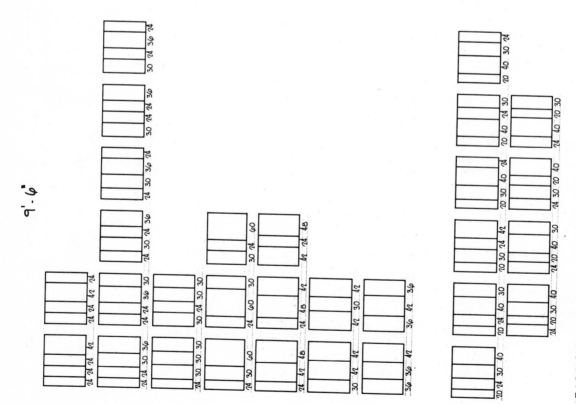

FIGURE D-5.   COMBINATION AT 9'-4" AND 9'-6" WITH EIGHT PRODUCT SIZES mullion will then total ⅞ inch over a 4-inch multiple dimension. For example, a 1′8⅞″ window plus a 3′0⅞″ window plus a 3⅛-inch mullion equals 5′0⅞″. Any additional windows would still leave the total ⅞ inch over a 4-inch multiple.

This additional ⅞ inch is awkward in panel construction of fixed multiples, where windows should fit to nonfractional dimensions which are multiples of the panels, such as 12′0″, and in masonry construction, where openings are one joint width wider than the multiple of bricks and joints spanning the opening. Thus, an opening might be 4′0⅜″, which would not accommodate a 4′0⅞″ window.

A possible solution is illustrated by the use of a standard aluminum window with details similar to those of the majority of windows manufactured in this country. The sections are designed so that the mullion may range in size from 2 inches to 3⅛ inches. The standard window sizes are 1′8⅞″, 2′0⅞″, 2′8⅞″, 3′4⅞″, 3′8⅞″, 4′0⅞″, and 4′8⅞″. If 2⅝ inches were used for the mullion size and ⅜ inch, instead of ⅞ inch, for the window, 3-inch flexibility would be obtained for masonry conditions. Examples of one or more windows fitting into a normal masonry opening are:

One window: 4′0⅜″

Two windows: 2′0⅜″ + 2⅝″ + 3′0⅜″ = 6′0⅜″
Three windows: 3′9⅜″ + 2⅝″ + 4′0⅜″ + 2⅝″ + 3′9⅜″ = 12′0⅜″

The two-window example is shown in the top half of Figure D-6.

In panel-type construction, however, windows must fit into a 3-inch multiple dimension, so an additional ⅜ inch must be removed or 2⅝ inches added. The windows above are shown in the lower half of Figure D-6 cut back for the panel condition. Details of another manufacturer's window, shown in Figure D-7, will give 2-inch flexibility when an extra edge section is used at each jamb to add 1⅝ inches to the additional ⅜ inch and bring the total dimension up to the next 2-inch increment for panel-type conditions.

These examples indicate that it is possible to develop a wide variety of window ranges, using standard extrusions and sections to give flexibility to any inch increment.

PLYWOOD PANELS

The most common size of softwood plywood panels is 4′0″ by 8′0″. The wood veneers for these panels are normally cut from 8′0″ peeler logs and

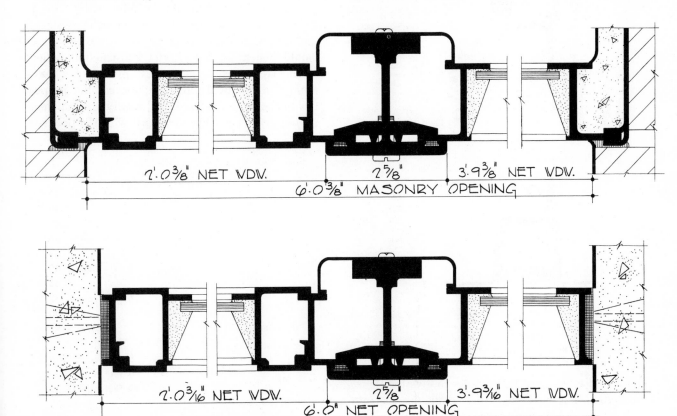

FIGURE D-6.   POSSIBLE ADJUSTMENT OF WINDOW SIZES TO FIT MASONRY OPENINGS

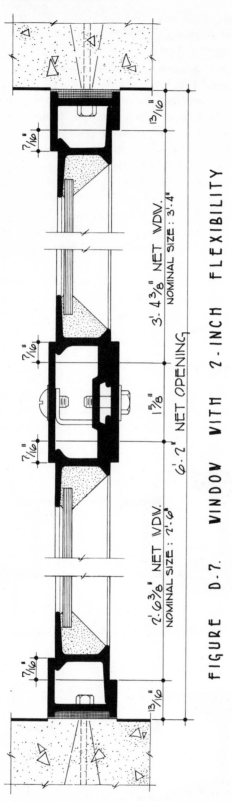

FIGURE D-7. WINDOW WITH 2-INCH FLEXIBILITY

2-foot widths, and the 5-foot panels into 20-inch and 40-inch widths. These six sizes would provide 4-inch design flexibility, and could be cut from the same standard size of raw material used today with no great change in production method.

The products involved in these three size ranges—movable partitions, windows, and plywood panels—can easily be used together and related to one another as shown in Figure D-1 even though their increments of flexibility are different. This development of component ranges can be extended to all wall, floor, ceiling, and roof components to provide a basis for interchangeability of all building components. This would make possible the effective production and use of standard products and would provide the architect with a substantial degree of design freedom.

Coordination achieved in this way would benefit all the people involved in the design and building process. The architect would have a design keyboard capable of infinite variety. The contractor would be able to make more accurate estimates and would save labor time on the job. The manufacturer would mass-produce a limited range of standard sizes. The local distributor would need to stock only a limited number of the standard components and would be able to offer better service. The owner would get an economically designed building with a greater potential for flexibility and would benefit from a shorter construction period.

The component ranges must provide for maximum mathematical flexibility, respect the properties of the materials used, and satisfy anthropometric requirements. The keyboard which is the com-

are glued together at right angles to give the panel strength. These veneers could easily be cut into 3-foot and 5-foot widths as well as into the two standard 4-foot widths. This would give three standard sizes of plywood, 3'0", 4'0", and 5'0" wide, with a resulting 1'0" flexibility in design. In addition, the 4-foot panels could be cut into two

Inches		Inches
1	3 feet equal	36
2		40
3		45
4	4 feet equal	48
5		54
6	5 feet equal	60
8		64
9	6 feet equal	72
10		80
1 foot equals 12		81
15		90
16	8 feet equal	96
18	9 feet equal	108
20	10 feet equal	120
2 feet equal 24		128
27		135
30	12 feet equal	144
32		

FIGURE D-8. DIMENSIONS OF GREATEST FLEXIBILITY FOR COMBINATION

posite of all the product ranges should provide for wall thickness and jointing problems which depend on small differences in size. It should provide guidance for the selection of window, door, panel, and other product sizes, and aid manufacturers in the determination of sizes for production. The use of a small base module gives little guidance in the development of a large panel, and confusion will result if these larger products are not related to each other and to many smaller ones. In view of these requirements, a geometric relationship is indicated in which the intervals are very small between the smaller sizes and increase as the sizes grow larger.

The Building Research Station in England has developed a method of choosing a group of dimensions for product sizes which is described in *The Modular Number Pattern,* by Professor Ehrenkrantz. The dimensions selected for the modular number pattern are those which are left when all the prime numbers (odd numbers which cannot be divided evenly) and their multiples above 5 are eliminated. These would be 7, 11, 13, 14, 17, etc. Those remaining, which have the greatest possible design flexibility, are shown in Figure D-8. As an example of this flexibility, 72 inches is a better choice for the size of a standard component than 73 inches because, although both can be divided

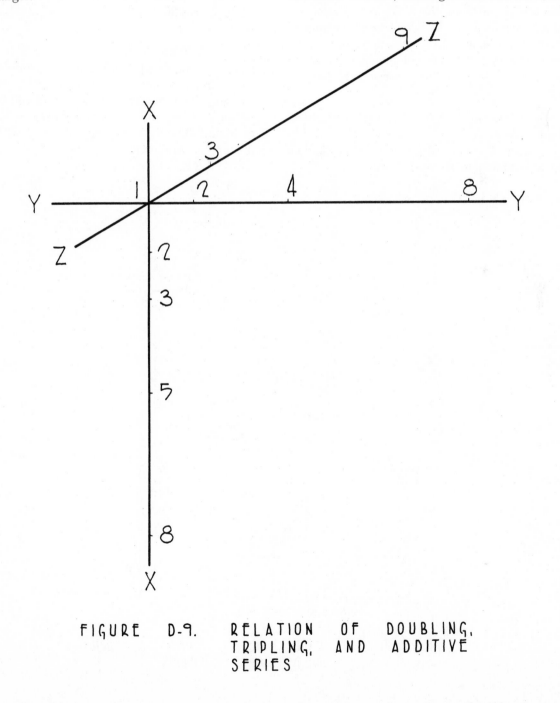

FIGURE D-9.   RELATION OF DOUBLING, TRIPLING, AND ADDITIVE SERIES

unequally in a number of ways, of the two, only 72 inches can be divided equally in several ways, as two 36's, three 24's, four 18's, or eight 9's. As building tends to be an additive process, products of equal size which can be added together are desirable.

The dimensions shown in Figure D-8 may be related in a three-dimensional grid to illustrate their interchangeable properties. Three simple arithmetic series are used for this: the doubling series (1, 2, 4, 8 . . .), the tripling series (1, 3, 9, 27 . . .), and the Fibonacci or additive series, in which the previous two numbers are added to give the next term in the series (1, 2, 3, 5, 8, 13 . . .). These three series, related on the *X*, *Y*, and *Z* axes, are shown in Figure D-9. In Figure D-10 the dimensions are filled in, and the result is the same dimensions shown in Figure D-8. Following are examples of the relations of the dimensions to one another:

1. To halve, move left, e.g., 90 in III, Column B, to 45 in Column A.

2. To third, move forward, e.g., 90 in III, Column B, to 30 in same position in II, Column B.

3. To add two unequal dimensions, move down, e.g., 36 and 54 in III, Column B, equal 90.

4. 90, which is equal to three 30's, is also equal to 30 + 60, in II, Column B + Column C.

5. 60 is also equal to four 15's, obtained by moving two columns to the left in II, Column C to Column A.

6. In III, Column A, 45 equals three 15's; therefore 60 equals 15 + 45, and 90, which equals 30 + 60, is therefore equal to 15 + 30 + 45.

7. 45, in III, Column A, may also be broken down into the two numbers immediately above it, 27 and 18. This breakdown of numbers may continue indefinitely, e.g., 27 equals three 9's, 18 equals three 6's, 60 equals 36 + 24, 24 equals two 12's, three 8's, and 16 + 8.

The thirty-three numbers between 1 inch and 12 feet in the number pattern should be considered as the basis for product sizes and not as planning dimensions. Although these numbers should be used as much as possible for product sizes, because of their flexibility they may be combined with sizes that are not in the number pattern when others are required to meet specific problems.

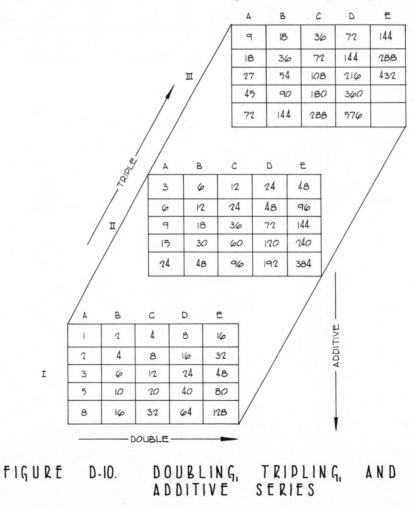

III

A	B	C	D	E
9	18	36	72	144
18	36	72	144	288
27	54	108	216	432
45	90	180	360	
72	144	288	576	

II

A	B	C	D	E
3	6	12	24	48
6	12	24	48	96
9	18	36	72	144
15	30	60	120	240
24	48	96	192	384

I

A	B	C	D	E
1	2	4	8	16
2	4	8	16	32
3	6	12	24	48
5	10	20	40	80
8	16	32	64	128

TRIPLE

ADDITIVE

DOUBLE

FIGURE D-10.   DOUBLING, TRIPLING, AND ADDITIVE SERIES

There are a number of approaches to the problem of selecting a group of product sizes to give a specific increment of flexibility. Where the products are cut from a larger sheet, it is desirable that there be no waste of the original material. When each product size is made separately, this requirement does not apply. An example of one approach to this problem is given by Figure D-11, in which are shown combinations of four to six product sizes which give various increments of flexibility.

With a basis for developing ranges of building products which provide considerable design flexibility and which relate to each other, thought may be given to the coordination of the entire building industry. The major problem is the incorporation of this material into design. A principle already established states that building products which are made by machine should not be cut by hand at the building site. Under present methods of construction, a contractor must often figure a wastage of 20 per cent for some materials because of the job-site requirements of cutting and fitting. If the architect has designed the building so that no cutting and fitting are required, the extra profit is absorbed by the contractor. A method is needed, therefore, to point out in working drawings when standard materials are used and when they are not. A variation of the dot and arrow system used for modular dimensioning might be employed in which arrows indicated a standard component and dots indicated one which must be cut. The drawings would then inform the contractor specifically where no cutting was required. He could figure his bid more closely and pass the saving on to the owner.

This distinction between standard and nonstandard materials is more important than whether products are on or off a reference grid. It would be possible, for example, to design a building on a 4-inch reference grid using arrows only, but without a single standard product and with no modular coordination involved. A better solution would be the use of four symbols, two for standard and nonstandard products, and two to relate the products to the reference grid.

An example of the way in which this flexibility might be used is shown in Figure D-12. The interior partitions of a typical classroom wing are made from four sizes which provide 4-inch design flexibility: 24, 36, 40, and 48 inches. The roof rests on the exterior walls, and the interior partitions are movable. If a change in educational requirements necessitates a revision of the interior arrangement, it can be achieved with the same interior partition panels, as shown in Figure D-13.

This approach does not require the elimination of any current philosophy of modular coordination. New modular components sized to various intervals of 4 inches could become a part of larger product ranges, each with its own increment of flexibility Once 4-inch flexibility is obtained, manufacturers may find that they can easily give 2-inch flexibility with the products that they are producing and so achieve greater variety.

The two important concepts which should be applied are (1) that small increments of flexibility must be obtained with large products, and (2) that these products must be used without alteration at the building site.

Base dimension	24	27	30	32	36	40	45	48	54	60	64	72	80	81	90	96	108	120	128	135	144
Half	12	13½	15	16	18	20	22½	24	27	30	32	36	40	40½	45	48	54	60	64	67½	72
One-third and two-thirds	8 16	9 18	10 20	... ...	12 24	... ...	15 30	16 32	18 36	20 40	... ...	24 48	... ...	27 54	30 60	32 64	36 72	40 80	... ...	45 90	48 96
Fibonacci pair	9 15	... ...	12 18	12 20	13½ 22½	16 24	18 27	18 30	... ...	24 36	24 40	27 45	32 48	... ...	36 54	36 60	... ...	48 72	48 80	54 81	54 90
					Increment of flexibility which may be obtained above the base dimension																
	3 4	4½	3 5	4	4½ 6	4	3 4½	4 6	9	4 6 10	8	3	8	...	6 9 15	4	18	8 12	...	9	12

The groups of products are taken vertically, and the smaller sizes are cut from the base dimension. The increment of flexibility of the group of products is shown at the bottom of the chart, and this flexibility begins from the base dimension upwards.

FIGURE D-11. INCREMENTS OF FLEXIBILITY FOR SMALL GROUPS OF PRODUCTS

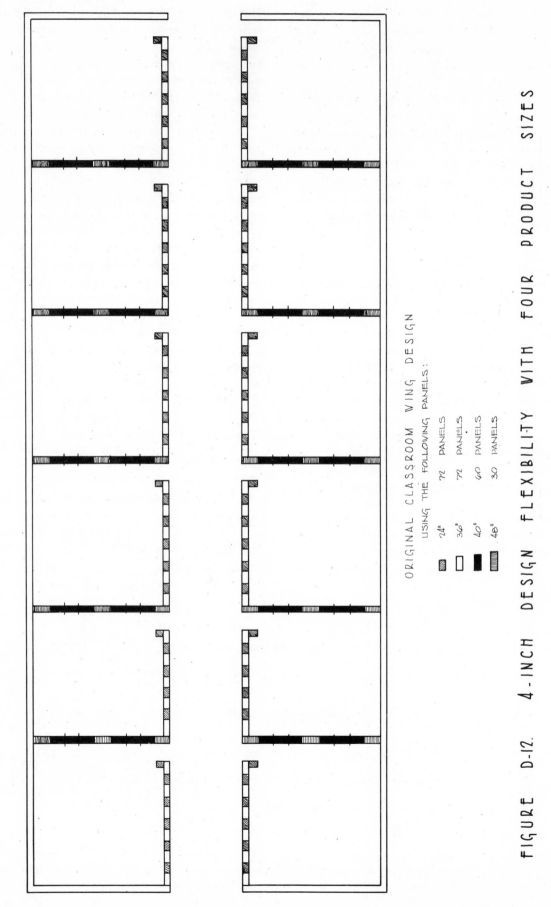

ORIGINAL CLASSROOM WING DESIGN

USING THE FOLLOWING PANELS:

24"	72	PANELS
36"	72	PANELS
40"	60	PANELS
48"	30	PANELS

FIGURE D-12.   4-INCH DESIGN FLEXIBILITY WITH FOUR PRODUCT SIZES

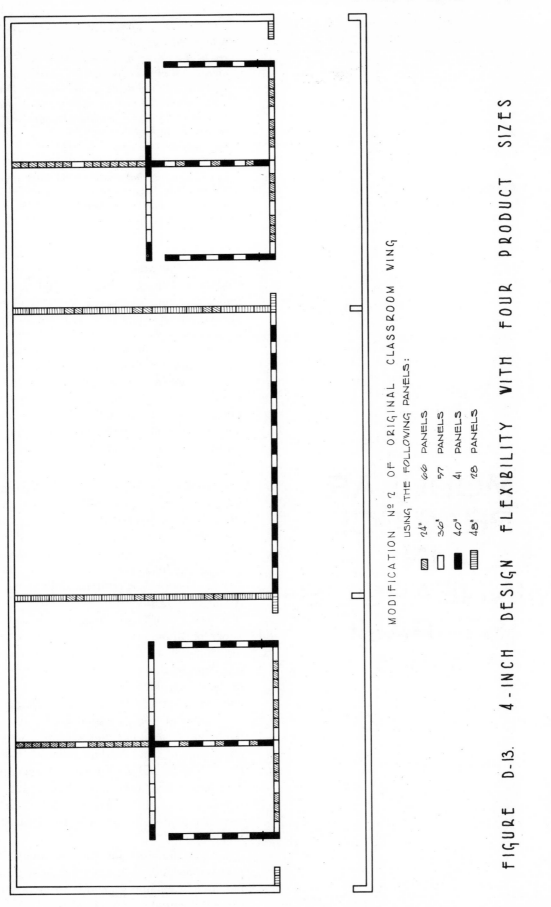

MODIFICATION Nº 2 OF ORIGINAL CLASSROOM WING
USING THE FOLLOWING PANELS:

24"   66 PANELS
36"   57 PANELS
40"   41 PANELS
48"   18 PANELS

FIGURE D-13. 4-INCH DESIGN FLEXIBILITY WITH FOUR PRODUCT SIZES

In March of 1959, a survey conducted by the Modular Building Standards Association showed that the area centered on Minneapolis–St. Paul in Minnesota was far ahead of the rest of the country in the use of modular practice in architectural offices and in construction. A follow-up questionnaire to the architects of this area in December, 1960, confirmed this fact and led to a meeting of the Chief Editor of **Modular Practice** *with representatives of the Minnesota Society of Architects of the American Institute of Architects, the Producers' Council, and the Associated General Contractors to discuss the impact of modular practice on the building industry in the Minneapolis–St. Paul area. Appendix E is a summary of the results of this discussion, held in January, 1961.*

APPENDIX E

MODULAR PRACTICE IN MINNEAPOLIS- ST. PAUL AREA

Between 25 and 30 per cent of the architectural offices in the Minneapolis–St. Paul area use full modular practice extensively, including modular design and coordination, and modular dimensioning of working drawings. In addition, another 10 to 15 per cent of the offices use the principles of modular design but do not follow all the way through with modular dimensioning, and another 5 to 10 per cent would use modular practice if they were given adequate information on conversion. This extensive use of, and interest in, modular practice has had a definite influence on the practice of architecture and the construction of buildings in the area.

1. Modular design, modular drawings, and modular construction are widely accepted and understood by contractors. Neither the architects nor the Associated General Contractors' headquarters have received any questions from contractors concerning modular construction since the middle 1950's. The work is built as designed with no confusion or difficulty.

2. The majority of architects do not use grid paper or draw grids extensively on the working drawings. They think in terms of modular dimensions and modular components from the beginning of the design stage, and indicate only the necessary and important grid lines in their drawings.

3. Although the structural engineers do not attempt to use modular dimensioning in their drawings, many of them do show the grids indicated by the architects, and dimension from the structure to grid lines where necessary. Beams and columns, which are usually shown with actual dimensions, are thus related to the modular drawings of the architect.

4. Shop drawings for modular projects are prepared in a standard manner with actual dimensions but usually include grid lines to give reference to the architectural working drawings.

5. The mason-training program of the Associated General Contractors reflects the influence of the attitude toward modular practice in a number of ways. Modular bricks are used in the preapprenticeship school; there is a related training program on the reading of modular plans and estimating from them; and the supervisory classes for carpenter superintendents and bricklayer foremen are conducted at times by architects who go over modular details and help in the reading of modular plans.

6. Modular rules are widely used on the job site by masons, and because joint sizes are always the same there is never any question or problem about varying these sizes to coordinate masonry with other materials.

The general impression given by construction-industry personnel is that modular practice is a widely understood and accepted design and building technique, which has grown familiar from its increasing use over a period of more than ten years. The opinion of the majority was that modular practice had benefited the construction industry in the area and would prove even more valuable as it was accepted on a continually widening basis.

David A. Pierce, AIA

APPENDIX F

SYSTEMS
OF
PROPORTION

Systems or theories of proportion are closely allied to the whole theory of architectural design and were included in the earliest known writings on architecture by Vitruvius in 27 B.C. The fundamentals of architecture found in these early writings are valid today; however, the method of their application has varied down through the ages. From evidence seen in the buildings left standing or contained in writings, some system of proportion seems to have been developed which provided a guide to the architects of each age.

If the Egyptians and Greeks left writings on architecture, they have not yet been found, leaving the evidence of their theories standing as buildings for later generations to discover for themselves the secret of the system or theory if there was one. The results of the studies of these earlier buildings by scholars of many periods of history indicate that there is a consistent repetition of certain ratios of proportions for the size and spacing of the elements of the buildings, which seems to substantiate the existence of a system or theory of proportion.

The consistent repetition of certain ratios of proportion in architecture finds a parallel in the mathematics of the time (Pythagoras) and also in the arts. In Plato's *Timaeus*, "On the Divisions of the World-Soul into Harmonic Intervals" gives divine significance to the numbers 1, 2, 3, 4, 8, 9, and 27.

Other numbers of importance were the intervals between musical notes which were pleasing to the ear. The Greeks discovered that musical tones of a given frequency had a specific wave length and that the combinations of tones which were most pleasing to the ear, such as the octave (2:1), the fifth (3:2), and the fourth (4:3), produced consistent intervals and ratios of frequencies. There is no direct evidence that the Greeks translated either the "world-soul harmonic intervals" or the musical ratios into architectural ratios. However, later scholars did hold this idea.

The development of land measure and mathematics by Pythagoras seems to have had the greatest influence on Greek architecture. The development of mathematics produced a requirement for fractions which was not easily comprehended; therefore, the Greeks reduced the size of the unit of measure to eliminate the need for fractions. There being no bureau of standards to establish definite units of measure, each architect had to set a unit of measure or module for each project and he established a set of ratios so that the proportions of his building would not be destroyed by the use of different standards of units of measure on the job.

Vitruvius, a Roman architect and engineer, wrote of a system of proportion evolved from his study of Greek and Roman buildings. However, his writings are obscure because the exact meanings of the Latin words translated as symmetry and proportion are not known, and their meanings should be freely interpreted in the light of their usage. The writings of Vitruvius are set forth rather fully in the following pages because the principles he enumerated have influenced architecture down to the present day more than any other single collection of writings, either because he was all inclusive or because he left the final application of principles to the judgment and discretion of the reader.

Architecture depends on Order, Arrangement, Eurythmy, Symmetry, Propriety, and Economy.

Order gives due measure to the members of a work considered separately, and symmetrical agreement to the *proportions* of the whole. It is an adjustment according to quantity. By this I mean the selection of modules from the members of the work itself and, starting from these individual parts of members, constructing the whole work to correspond.

Arrangement includes the putting of things in their proper places and the elegance of effect which is due to adjustments appropriate to the character of the work. . . .

Eurythmy (eurhythmy) is beauty and fitness in the arrangements of the members. This is found when the members of a work are of a height suited to their breadth, of a breadth suited to their length, and, in a word, when they all correspond symmetrically (proportionally).

Symmetry is a proper arrangement between the members of the work itself, and relation between the different parts and the whole general scheme, in accordance with a certain part selected as standard. Thus in the human body there is a kind of symmetrical (proportional) harmony between forearm, foot, palm, finger, and other small parts; and so it is with perfect buildings. In the case of temples, symmetry may be calculated from the thickness of a column, from a triglyph, or even from a module. . . .*

Proceeding from his principles of architecture, he enunciates his principles of symmetry and proportion and then gives a detailed account of actual proportions of temples and the orders of architecture:

Proportion is a correspondence among the measures of the members of an entire work, and of the whole to a certain part selected as standard. From this result the principles of symmetry. Without *symmetry* and *proportion* there can be no principles in the design of any temple; that is, if there is no precise relation between its members as in the case of those of a well-shaped man.

* Vitruvius, Book I, Chapter II, p. 13: "The Fundamental Principles of Architecture." Full references for work cited in the footnotes of this chapter will be found in the bibliography on p. 194.

For the human body is so designed by nature that the face, from the chin to the top of the forehead and the lowest roots of the hair, is a tenth part of the whole height; the open hand from the wrist to the tip of the middle finger is just the same; the head from the chin to the crown is an eighth, and with the neck and shoulder from the top of the breast to the lowest roots of the hair is a sixth; from the middle of the breast to the summit of the crown is a fourth. If we take the height of the face itself, the distance from the bottom of the chin to the underside of the nostrils is one third of it; the nose from the underside of the nostrils to a line between the eyebrows is the same; from there to the lowest roots of the hair is also a third, comprising the forehead. The length of the foot is one sixth of the height of the body; of the forearm, one fourth; and the breadth of the breast is also one fourth. The other members, too, have their own symmetrical proportions, and it was by employing them that the famous painters and sculptors of antiquity attained to great and endless renown. . . .

Similarly, in the members of a temple there ought to be the greatest harmony in the symmetrical relations of the different parts to the general magnitude of the whole. . . .

Therefore, since nature has designed the human body so that its members are duly proportioned to the frame as a whole, it appears that the ancients had good reason for their rule, that in perfect buildings the different members must be in exact symmetrical (proportional) relations to the whole general scheme. Hence, while transmitting to us the proper arrangements for buildings of all kinds, they were particularly careful to do so in the case of temples of the gods, buildings in which merits and faults usually last forever.

Further, it was from the members of the body that they derived the fundamental ideas of the measures which are obviously necessary in all works, as the finger, palm, foot, and cubit. These they apportioned so as to form the "perfect number" . . . and as the perfect number the ancients fixed upon ten. For it is from the number of the fingers of the hand that the palm is found, and the foot from the palm. Again, ten is naturally perfect, as being made up by the fingers of the two palms. Plato also held that this number was perfect because ten is composed of the individual units. . . . But as soon as eleven or twelve is reached, the numbers, being excessive, cannot be perfect until they come to ten for the second time; for the component parts of that number are the individual units.

The mathematicians, however, maintaining a different view, have said that the perfect number is six, because this number is composed of integral parts which are suited numerically to their method of reckoning. . . .

And further, as the foot is one sixth of a man's height, the height of the body is expressed in number of feet being limited to six, they held that this was the perfect number, and observed that the cut consisted of six palms, or of twenty-four fingers. This principle seems to have been followed by the states of Greece. . . .

But later observing that six and ten were both of them perfect numbers, they combined the two, and thus made the most perfect number, sixteen. They found their authority for this in the foot. For if we take two palms from the cubit, there remains the foot of four palms; but the palm contains four fingers. Hence the foot contains sixteen fingers. . . . [This same arbitrary reasoning obtained in money denominations as well.]

Therefore, if it is agreed that number was found out from the human fingers, and that there is a symmetrical correspondence between the members separately and the entire form of the body, in accordance with a certain part selected as standard, we can have nothing but respect for those who, in constructing temples of the immortal gods, have so arranged the members of the works that both the separate parts and the whole design may harmonize in their proportions and symmetry.†

. . . They measured the imprint of a man's foot and compared this with his height. On finding that, in a man, the foot is one sixth of the height, they applied the same principle to the column, and reared the shaft, including the capital, to a height six times its thickness at its base. Thus the Doric column, as used in buildings, began to exhibit the proportions, strength, and beauty of the body of a man.

Just so afterwards, when they desired to construct a temple to Diana in a new style of beauty, they translated these footprints into terms characteristic of the slenderness of women, and thus first made a column the thickness of which was only one eighth of its height, so that it might have a taller look. . . . Thus in the invention of the two different kinds of columns, they borrowed manly beauty, naked and unadorned, for the one, and for the other the delicacy, adornment, and proportions characteristic of women. ‡

It is not impossible, however, that in all theatres these rules of symmetry should answer all conditions and purposes, but the architect ought to consider to what extent he must follow the principle of symmetry, and to what extent it may be modified to suit the nature of the site or the size of the work. There are, of course, some things which, for utilities sake, must be made of the same size in a small theatre, and a large one: such as the steps, curved cross-aisles, their parapets, the passages, stairways, stages, tribunals, and any other things which occur that make it necessary to give up symmetry so as not to interfere with utility . . . it will not be amiss to make a slight reduction or addition, provided that it is done without going too far, but with intelligence. This will be possible, if the architect is a man of practical experience, and besides, not destitute of cleverness and skill. §

There is nothing to which an architect should devote more thought than to the exact proportions of his building with reference to a certain part selected as the standard. After the standard of symmetry has been determined, and the proportionate dimensions adjusted by calculations, it is next the part of wisdom to consider the nature of the site, or questions of use or beauty and modify the plan by diminutions or additions in such a manner that these diminutions or additions in the symmetrical relations may be seen to be made on correct principles, and without detracting at all from the effect.

† Vitruvius, Book III, Chapter I, pp. 72–75: "On Symmetry: In Temples and in the Human Body."

‡ Vitruvius, Book IV, Chapter I, p. 103: "The Origins of the Three Orders and the Proportions of the Corinthian Capitals."

§ Vitruvius, Book V, Chapter VI, p. 148: "On the Subject of the Design of Theatres."

The look of a building when seen close at hand is one thing, on a height it is another, not the same in an enclosed place, still different in the open, and in all these cases it takes much judgment to decide what is to be done. The fact that the eye does not always give a true impression, but very often leads the mind to form a false judgment . . . whether this appearance is due to the impact of the images, or to the effusion of the rays from the eye, as the physicists hold, in either case it is obvious that the vision may lead us to false impressions.

Since, therefore, the reality may have a false appearance, and since things are sometimes represented by the eyes as other than they are, I think it certain that diminutions or additions should be made to suit the nature or needs of the site, but in such fashion that the buildings lose nothing thereby. These results, however, are also attainable by flashes of genius, and not only by mere science.

Hence, the first thing to settle is the standard of symmetry, from which we need not hesitate to vary. Then, lay out the ground lines of the length and breadth of the work proposed, and when once we have determined its size, let the construction follow this with due regard to beauty of proportion, so that the beholder may feel no doubt of the eurythmy of its effect. ‖

RENAISSANCE PROPORTION SYSTEMS

The essence of the Renaissance systems of proportion was that architecture was considered a science and that each side of a building, inside as well as outside, had to be integrated into one and the same system of mathematical ratios. The architect was not free to apply a system of his own choosing. The ratio had to comply with conceptions of a higher order, and the ratios of the building constructed should reflect the proportions of the human body. Since man is the image of God and the proportions of his body are produced by the divine will, so the proportions in architecture should embrace and express the cosmic order.

Alberti (1404–1472), an Italian architect, painter, philosopher, musician, and author, produced the first major writings since Vitruvius on the proportions of architecture in his *De re aedificatoria,* published in 1485. The essence of Alberti's theory of proportion included the basic concept of mathematics and music as first expressed by Pythagoras: "The numbers by means of which the agreement of sounds affects our ears with delight, are the very same which please our eyes and our minds." ¶ This doctrine remained fundamental to the whole Renaissance system of proportion: "We shall therefore borrow all our rules for harmonic relations from the musicians to whom this sort of numbers is

‖ Vitruvius, Book VI, Chapter II, p. 174: "Symmetry, and Modifications in It to Suit the Site."

¶ Wittkower (1949, 1952).

extremely well known, and from those particular things wherein nature shows herself most excellent and complete. . . ." Alberti also stated that the architect who relies on these harmonies is not translating musical ratios into architecture but is making use of a universal harmony apparent in music.

Palladio (1518–1580) founded most of his theory of proportion on the writings of Vitruvius and used a unit of measure which he applied to all dimensions in a building. In some cases it was the diameter of a small column or the width of a pilaster, and simple ratios of whole numbers of the same modulus were effective throughout his buildings. He went back to the ideas of Pythagoras and Plato and adhered to the number series 1, 2, 3, 4, 8, 9, and 27.

. . . Whatever one may think of Palladio's façades, it must be admitted that they represent the climax of a development to which, significantly, the great classical architects Alberti, Bramante and Peruzzi had contributed. It is not surprising, therefore, that Palladio's solution proved to be one of the outstanding European successes and that it was adopted and copied for 250 years. ¶

Palladio's later work reflects a meticulous care in employing harmonic ratios not only on the inside of each single room but also in the relation of rooms to each other as well as to the exterior of the building and the building as a whole. He developed his architecture and complicated his harmonic ratios as the concept of music developed during his lifetime.

Renaissance applications of musical ratios and visual-measurement ratios continued on a rigid and narrow path which, as stated above, left the architect little choice in his designs.

Late in the seventeenth century, however, rebellion against this rigidity began to appear. One of the first strong opposers was Claude Perrault (*Ordonnance des cinq especes des colonnes*, 1683), who broke decisively with the conception that certain ratios were *a priori* beautiful and declared that proportions which follow "the rules of architecture" were agreeable for no other reason than that people were used to them. Consequently, he advocated the relativity of our aesthetic judgment and quite logically turned against the idea that musical consonances can be translated into visual proportions. This rebellion was reflected further by Temanza, who agreed that in the widest sense numbers regulate buildings as well as music. He insisted on commensurability throughout the structure; but argued that otherwise proportion in music and in architecture are widely different. His criticism of the general applicability of musical con-

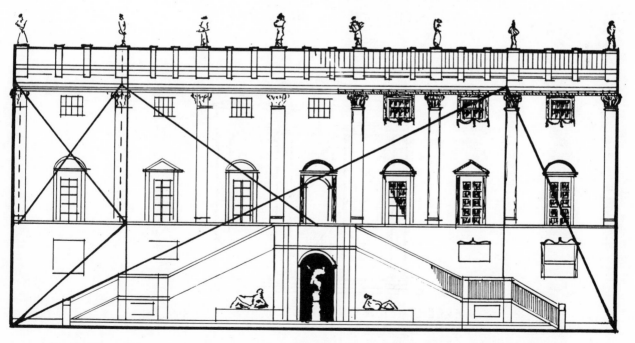

FIGURE F-I   MICHELANGELO. CAPITAL AT ROME.
CORBUSIER'S "PLACE OF THE RIGHT
ANGLE" APPLIED TO THE FACADE.

sonances to architecture can be reduced to two objections which reveal an entirely new viewpoint. The first objection is that the eye is not capable of perceiving simultaneously the ratios of length, width, and height of a room; and the second, that architectural proportions must be judged from the angle of vision by which the building is viewed. In other words, architectural proportions cannot be absolute, but must be relative. The emphasis has shifted from the objective truth of the building to the subjective truth of the perceiving individual.

Temanza contended that the use of harmonic proportions in architecture would lead to sterility.

The Baroque (Fr. bizarre or fantastic) was a new phase of architectural development, which, in later Renaissance times, was revealed first in Rome and afterwards spread throughout Europe. . . .

. . . It is sometimes called the Rococo style, and arose in the seventeenth century, when the true Renaissance had exhausted its energy and succumbed to the formal rules and monotonous regulations of schoolmen and classicists, notably Palladio and Vignola, who, however, were themselves greater than the rules they formu-

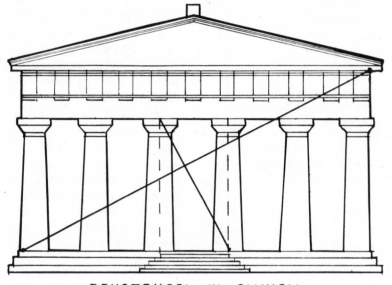

ZEUSTEMPEL IN OLYMPIA

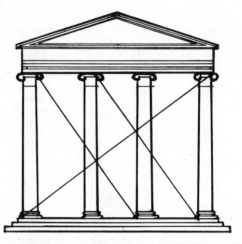

ERECHTHEION IN ATHENS, NORTH FRONT

FIGURE F-2   ANALYSIS OF CLASSICAL BUILDINGS BY WÖLFFLIN. (FROM HEINRICH WÖLFFLIN'S KLEINE SCHRIFTEN, 1946)

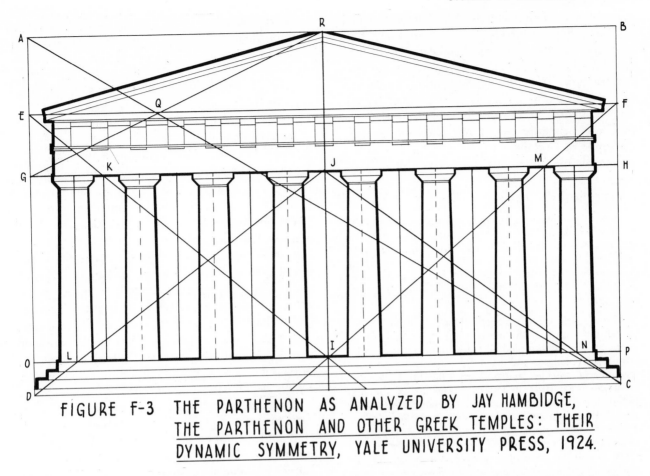

FIGURE F-3 THE PARTHENON AS ANALYZED BY JAY HAMBIDGE, THE PARTHENON AND OTHER GREEK TEMPLES: THEIR DYNAMIC SYMMETRY, YALE UNIVERSITY PRESS, 1924.

lated. The Baroque was perhaps chiefly the outcome of reaction against the blind worship of Vitruvius, the Roman architect of the Augustan age, who had laid down rules and whose latter-day sixteenth-century disciples handed out prescriptions for building which killed the vital spark of the true Renaissance spirit. . . . The bookish formality in design had tended to reduce architecture to a lifeless product uninspiring in aspect, against which it is not surprising that the beauty-loving Italians should after a time have risen in revolt. They were weary of lifeless conventions, and they rose against the tyranny of stereotyped rules and standards of proportions. They demanded freedom—freedom in plan, in design, and in ornament. . . . The Baroque style at its best was an assertion of freedom, and at its worst a lapse into license. . . .

There was often a straining after originality for its own sake which was apt to detract from the general unity of the design. . . .

The Baroque movement, in spite of its many and glaring defects, has perhaps been treated too harshly by critics, who have seized upon its faults without realizing its genesis, as a breaking away from a type of architecture which had suppressed any efforts in novelty of design. . . .

Sir William Chambers (A.D. 1726–96) had the distinction of being the first Treasurer of the Royal Academy, while his "Treatise on the Decorative Part of Civil Architecture" is still a guide for architects, especially as regards the proportions of the Orders. . . . He adhered to the Anglo-Palladian traditions during the Greek Revival, and his work is correct and refined. . . .

The publication of "Inigo Jones Designs" by Kent, and "The Architecture of Andrea Palladio," with notes of I. Jones, by Leoni in A.D. 1742, and "Antiquities of Rome," which had been first published at Venice in A.D. 1554, were sarcastically referred to by Pope:

You show us Rome was glorious, not profuse
And pompous buildings once were things of use.
Yet shall, My Lord, your just, your noble rules,
Fill half the land with imitating fools;
Who random drawings from your sheets shall take,
And of one beauty many blunders make;
Load some vain church with old theatric state,
Turn arcs of triumph to a garden gate.[**]

A rage for symmetry and for ornate interiors too often dominated the design, regardless of internal comfort and convenience, especially in the large manors, and this phase of building design was also satirized by Pope:

'Tis very fine,
But where d'ye sleep, or where d'ye dine?
I find by all you have been telling,
That 'tis a house, but not a dwelling.

DEVELOPMENT OF MODERN SYSTEMS OF PROPORTION

During the nineteenth century, numerous theories of proportion appeared; however, there was little

[**] Fletcher (1931), pp. 599, 600, 782.

agreement as to the methods of arriving at the final solution. Some methods based on an analysis of past construction were so complicated that they could not be applied in a process of designing new construction. Most of the systems of proportion in the nineteenth century were stimulated by the revival of Greek and Gothic architecture. The attitude was primarily one of rediscovering the true principles of Greek and Gothic architecture with a fresh new application, and not merely blind copying.

John Ruskin indicates:

It is utterly vain to endeavor to reduce proportion to finite rules, for it is as various as musical melody, and the laws to which it is subject are of the same general kind; so that the determination of right or wrong proportion is as much a matter of feeling and experience as the appreciation of good musical composition. . . .††

The French writer Viollet-le-Duc analyzed Gothic proportion based on the use of three different kinds of triangles: the right-angled isosceles triangle, the familiar equilateral triangle, and what he calls the "Egyptian" triangle, an isosceles triangle with a height of 2½ parts compared to a base of 4 parts. The use of the first two of these in design is more or less equivalent to the use of 45 degree and 30 degree-60 degree set-squares, a fact which is apparent in many of Viollet-le-Duc's illustrations. This system of proportion tends to generate the triple geometric progression based on the numbers square-root 3, 1 plus square-root 3 and 2 as its characteristic pattern of proportional relationships.‡‡

Both Viollet-le-Duc and Ruskin objected to the fixed proportions of the Renaissance and saw no difficulty in the use of variable proportions based on mathematics.

Although Vitruvius and Alberti had implied the importance of the principle of the repetitions of ratios in architectural design, Barca in Italy and later Lloyd in England emphasized the importance of this principle rather than the indispensability of the ratios themselves. The development of mathematics and various numbers series did not influence architectural thinking until the φ (phi) series or Fibonacci series and its relationship to the "golden section" were noticed. The Fibonacci series 0, 1, 1, 2, 3, 5, 8, 13, 21, . . . contains the ratio 1.618 as the numbers increase, which is the ratio of the golden section, 1:1.618.

With triangles, pentagons, stars, and circles Lund and Moessel developed *geometrical systems* of proportion. These were branded as "beautiful approximations" which produced intriguing analyses of ancient buildings but were not practical for new design work.

Harry Roberts devised another geometrical system for use in architectural practice which included a series of set-squares enabling the architect to master several systems of proportion. However, because of its complication Roberts' system required a lot of study and experience for effective use and therefore did not gain general acceptance.

Sir Edwin Lutyens used the repetition of similar figures in his practice, beginning with the φ rectangle (1:1.618) and later changing to the square-root-of-2 rectangle (1:1.414). He worked not with rigid ratios but with ratios that suited his purpose.

The *analytical systems of proportion* are those which allow the architect to design repetition of similar shapes by proportional relationships between linear dimensions. William Schooling stressed the importance of additive properties of geometric progression, particularly the φ series. He devised a "universal φ scale" which consisted of parallel lines divided in a graduated series of φ scales so that the user could select any scale to suit his purpose and the proportion ratios would always be similar and related to φ.

Hambidge examined a great number of Greek vases to reconstruct the Greek system of proportion. He found the largest number of vases based on the square-root-of-5 and the φ-series ratios. In his examples in *Elements of Dynamic Symmetry*, the dimensions are expressed very simply in terms of φ and the square-root-of-5 or θ and the square-root-of-2. However, Hambidge rejects the use of these symbols because, he states, the Greeks used a method of geometry to obtain their results.

The most recent system of proportion to gain widespread consideration is that developed by Le Corbusier from human dimensions. In *The Modulor,* he states:

The "Modulor" is a measuring tool based on the human body and on mathematics. A man-with-arm-upraised provides, at the determining points of his occupation of space-foot, solar plexus, head, tips of fingers of the upraised arm—three intervals which give rise to a series of golden sections called the Fibonacci series. On the other hand, mathematics offers the simplest and also the most powerful variation of a value: the single unit, the double unit, and the three golden sections.§§

Einstein wrote regarding the "Modulor": "It is a scale of proportions which makes the bad difficult and the good easy . . . it makes your task more certain."

The "Modulor" consists of a "blue" scale which is double the "red" scale based on the φ series. These scales are related to the human figure in vari-

---

†† Ruskin (1849, 1898).
‡‡ Scholfield (1958).

§§ Le Corbusier (1954, 1958).

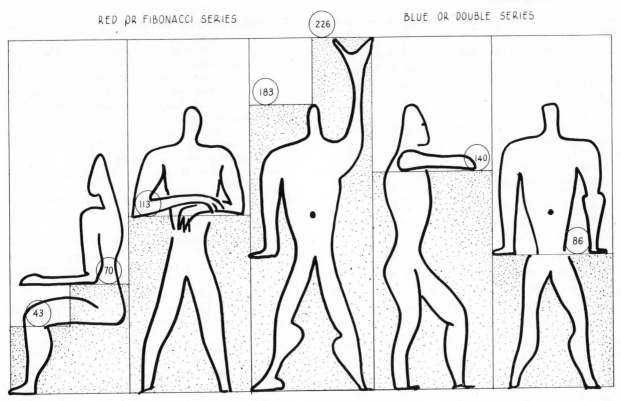

RED OR FIBONACCI SERIES

BLUE OR DOUBLE SERIES

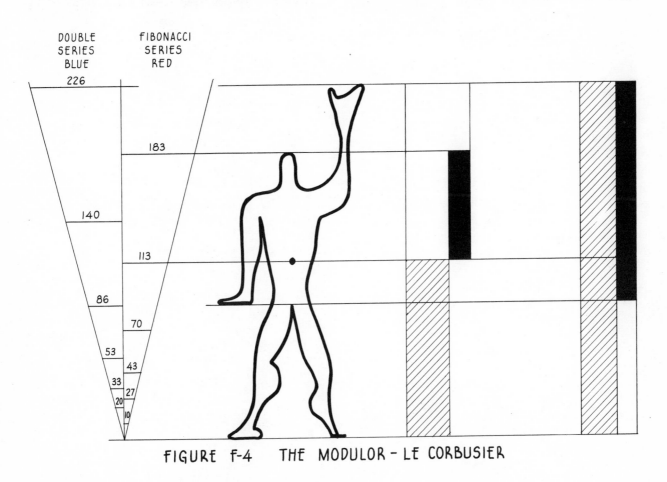

FIGURE F-4   THE MODULOR – LE CORBUSIER

ous positions. The "Modulor" can be expressed in dimensions of ½-inch units or centimeters which bridge the gap between the foot and inch system of measurement and the metric system. "The Modulor converts meters into feet and inches automatically." §§

The "Modulor" is not only an instrument of architectural proportion, it is a means of ensuring the repetition of similar shapes. It is also a system of preferred dimensions intended for standardizing the sizes of mass-produced building components.‖‖

Le Corbusier applies the "Modulor" to the parts of buildings, relying on their proper relationships to produce unity of the whole.

The pace and economics of present-day construction activity make the development of a repetitive system of architecture mandatory. Contemporary designers have unlimited materials and construction techniques, as compared with the past. This freedom makes it more important now than ever before that the architect develop a discipline for himself, or he will create a jungle of monotony and chaos.

‖‖ Scholfield (1958).

BIBLIOGRAPHY FOR APPENDIX F

Fletcher, Sir Banister, A History of Architecture on the Comparative Method, Charles Scribner's Sons, New York, and B. T. Batsford, London, ninth edition, 1931.

Hambidge, Jay, The Parthenon, Yale University Press, New Haven, Conn., and Humphrey Milford, Oxford University Press, London, 1924.

Le Corbusier, Creation Is a Patient Search, translated by James Palmes, Frederick A. Praeger, New York, 1951.

Le Corbusier, The Modulor, translated by Peter DeFrancia and Anna Bostock, Harvard University Press, Cambridge, Mass., 1954.

Le Corbusier, Modulor 2, translated by Peter DeFrancia and Anna Bostock, Harvard University Press, Cambridge, Mass., 1958.

Plato, Timaeus, translated by Francis M. Cornford, edited by Oskar Piest, The Liberal Arts Press, New York, 1959.

Ruskin, John, Modern Painters, 1843–60; new edition in 6 volumes, London, 1898. The Seven Lamps of Architecture, London, 1849.

Scholfield, P. H., The Theory of Proportion in Architecture, The Syndics of the Cambridge University Press, London, 1958.

Vitruvius, The Ten Books of Architecture, translated by Morris Hickey Morgan, Constable and Company, London, 1914, and Dover Publications, New York, 1960.

Wittkower, Rudolf, Architectural Principles in the Age of Humanism, London, 1949; second edition, 1952.

INDEX

DATE DUE

AG 20 '65		
DE 7 '65		
AP 26 '66		
AP 27 '67		
MY 24 '67		
MY 11 '68		
MR 15 '70		
MR 16 '70		
MY 30 '73		
OC 17 '73		
NOV 30 1980		
FEB 28 1983		
MAY 13 '85		
FEB 9 '87		

| D8 | Fordham Equip. Co. | |